Simcha's Kinder Torah

Torah Stories and Thoughts
On the Weekly Parasha
To Enhance Your Shabbos Table

Rabbi Simcha Groffman

Feldheim Publishers
Jerusalem / New York

Other works by the same author:

Simcha's Torah Stories (Targum Press)
You Left Mitzraim
Kinder Torah (A weekly parsha sheet)

First Published 2003
Copyright © 2003 by Simcha Groffman

All rights reserved
ISBN 1-58330-658-7

No part of this publication may be translated, reproduced, stored in retrieval system, or transmitted in any form or by any means, electronic, mechanical, photocopying, recording, or otherwise without prior permission in writing from the copyright holder.

Editor: Rabbi Shmuel Globus
Illustrations: Tova Katz

Please direct all inquiries to the author:
Rabbi Simcha Groffman
Email: simcha_b@netvision.net.il
POB 5338
Jerusalem, Israel
91052

Distributed by:
Feldheim Publishers
Box 35002
Jerusalem, Israel

200 Airport Executive Park
Nanuet, N. Y. 10954

Printed in Israel

Contents

Sefer Bereshis

☙ *Parashas Bereishis*
Heavy Duty Tools... 3
Mass Destruction.. 7

☙ *Parashas Noach*
Your Mitzvos, Your Children..................................... 8
Up The Down-Escalator..11

☙ *Parashas Lech Lecha*
Let's Make a Person... 14
Change the World... 16

☙ *Parashas Vayera*
Bring Out the Best in You.. 18
The Visit That Heals... 20

☙ *Parashas Chayei Sara*
Say a Little, Do a Lot... 23
What Did You Accomplish Today? 28

☙ *Parashas Toldos*
The Pipeline... 29
Who's Really Right? 33

☙ *Parashas Vayetze*
A Dream Ending... 35
The Well... 36

☙ *Parashas Vayishlach*
The Home.. 39
Honoring Parents... 43

☙ *Parashas Vayeshev*
Blockbuster.. 44

☙ *Parashas Miketz*
Turnaround..50

He's Paying Attention...53

❧ *Parashas Vayigash*
The Right Address...55
Gratitude..58
Forgive and Live...60

❧ *Parashas Vayechi*
A Good Education..61
Give Him Honor...63
Tell Them You Love Them..66

Sefer Shemos

❧ *Parashas Shemos*
Holy Ground..71

❧ *Parashas Va'eira*
Learn the Lesson..76
The Voice of Peace...79

❧ *Parashas Bo*
You Become What You Do......................................81
Unforgettable...84

❧ *Parashas Beshallach*
Our Protector...86
Mitzvos Are Forever..87
Always in the Sea...89

❧ *Parashas Yisro*
The Proper Setting..91
Like Any Other Mitzvah..94

❧ *Parashas Mishpatim*
Damage Control...97
Compromise...100

❧ *Parashas Terumah*
Beautiful Music...104
Give and Take..105

◌ *Parashas Tetzaveh*
  Guiding Light...108
  Holy Garments..111

◌ *Parashas Ki Sisa*
  The Sign..113
  Mercy..115

◌ *Parashas Vayakhel*
  Don't Wait Till The End...117
  Make a Name for Yourself..120

◌ *Parashas Pikudei*
  Who's Counting?..122
  The Wise Heart..124
  Trustworthiness..125

Sefer Vayikra

◌ *Parashas Vayikra*
  Come Closer..131
  Don't Embarrass..133
  Humility...134

◌ *Parashas Tzav*
  The Vessel..136
  Look Carefully...139

◌ *Parashas Shemini*
  Soul Building...144
  Rotten Bones..145
  It's Hard For Me..149

◌ *Parashas Tazria*
  The Projectile...150
  What A Welcome...151
  Keep Them Pure..153

◌ *Parashas Metzora*
  The Craftsman..155
  The Trickster..157

◊ *Parashas Acharei Mos*
　No Exceptions to the Rule...159

◊ *Parashas Kedoshim*
　The List...164
　Like Yourself...165
　Giving Brings Love..167

◊ *Parashas Emor*
　Mr. Ambassador..169
　The City of Happiness...173

◊ *Parashas Behar*
　Costly Words..176
　Shmitta...179

◊ *Parashas Bechukosai*
　Are You Listening?..181
　Keep Your Word..183

Sefer Bamidbar

◊ *Parashas Bamidbar*
　The Center..189
　Your Number...191

◊ *Parashas Nasso*
　No More, No Less..194
　Man's Best Friend...197

◊ *Parashas Beha'aloscha*
　School's Out..200
　Always At Home..204

◊ *Parashas Shelach*
　The Outsider..207
　Ladders to Heaven...209

◊ *Parashas Korach*
　It Always Spells Trouble..213
　It's Not My Job...215

∾ *Parashas Chukas*
   I Want To Speak To The Boss 219
   The Value of Shalom 223

∾ *Parashas Balak*
   Obsession 225
   Dignity 229

∾ *Parashas Pinchas*
   No Strain, No Gain 232
   The Reward 235

∾ *Parashas Mattos*
   Forget About Anger 238
   Know Your Enemy 241

∾ *Parashas Masei*
   It Takes Time 243
   Selfish Flattery 245
   It Is Fair 246

Sefer Devarim

∾ *Parashas Devarim*
   Quit Stalling 253
   Because They Love You 257

∾ *Parashas Va'eschanan*
   Call Me Any Time 259
   Sparkling Conversation 261
   Guard Them 262
   Constant Mitzvos 264

∾ *Parashas Eikev*
   Who Did All Of This? 266
   Built To Last 268
   Trust The Boss 270

∾ *Parashas Re'eh*
   Take Care Of Each Other 272

Hashem's Children 274
Togetherness 275

ଔ Parashas Shoftim
Assign Responsibility 277
The First 278
Good Habits 281

ଔ Parashas Ki Seitzei
Lost and Found 283
Family Gratitude 285
Compassion 287
Safety 288

ଔ Parashas Ki Savo
The Happy Mitzvos 290
The War 293
Pray for Me Too 294

ଔ Parashas Nitzavim
The Road Back 296
Wealthy Forever 298
Together As One 300

ଔ Parashas Vayelech
Everyone Is Going 302
A Personal Visit 304
The Shadow 305

ଔ Parashas Haazinu
Listen Carefully 309
Your Place in History 311
Deep Meaning 312

ଔ Parashas Vezos Haberachah
Unconditional Love 315
Strong Glue 317
United We Stand 318

Index 321

Simcha's Kinder Torah

Sefer Bereishis

Parashas Bereishis

Heavy Duty Tools

"*Oy vey*, my watch stopped again. I must get it fixed. Do you want to come along with me, Avi?"

"Sure, Chaim."

A short time later at the watch repair shop.

"Can I help you boys?"

"Yes sir, my watch stopped. Can you fix it?"

"Let's have a look and see what we can do. First, we will open the watch. There are four very small screws in the back. This very fine screwdriver will unscrew them. Now, the watch is open. Hmmm. There seems to be some dust here. I have a very small brush that sweeps away the dust nicely. Also, the battery is dead. Let's switch it for a fresh battery. We use this fine tweezers to take out the old battery and put in a new one. There we go. Everything seems to be working as good as new!"

"Thank you very much, sir. I could not help but notice how tiny and delicate your tools are."

"Watches are very small and compact. All of the parts are

miniaturized. Therefore, I need very small tools to work on the watches. If I were a carpenter, making tables and chairs, I would have much bigger tools."

"That makes sense, sir."

"Boys, did you ever see the tools that construction workers use? They are even bigger than a carpenter's tools. Construction workers are building buildings; a much bigger job that requires much bigger tools."

"Sir, last week I saw a steam shovel digging a hole in the ground to lay the foundations for a skyscraper."

"Now you are talking about a really big job, young man. For that, you need huge power tools like steam shovels and jackhammers. That reminds me of an auto trip that we took a few weeks ago. We were driving through the countryside and we saw a new road under construction. The workers were digging a tunnel through a mountain, using a gigantic digging machine. They also used tons of dynamite to blast their way through rock. That was a big job."

"Wow. That sounds fascinating. I have heard of even bigger construction projects, sir. Huge bridges that span great lengths, long tunnels under great bodies of water, huge dams that create man-made lakes. In some cases, they even move mountains. Can you imagine the size and power of the tools that they use for these construction projects?"

"Boys, those tools may seem big to you, but they are really just like tiny watchmaker's tools."

"What do you mean, sir?"

"You are speaking about building one bridge, one tunnel, or one building. A much bigger construction project many years ago dwarfed all of these structures."

"Are you speaking about the Brooklyn Bridge? The English Channel Tunnel? The Empire State Building? Boulder Dam? The Golden Gate Bridge?"

"Child's play! I am speaking about the creation of the world."

"You mean Parashas Bereishis. 'In the beginning, Hashem created the heaven and the earth' (*Bereishis* 1:1)."

"That's right, boys. Can you imagine the size of that construction project? Hashem created this entire world, with all of its great mountains and valleys, oceans and rivers, forests and deserts. Not only the earth, but all the plants and animals that inhabit it, from the tiniest one-celled creature to the mighty elephants and whales."

"That is mind-boggling, sir."

"There is more. Hashem created the entire universe: the sun, moon, and all of the stars. Billions and billions of stars, galaxies, planets, and worlds without number."

"Wow, what a tremendous construction project!"

"Just take a minute to think about something else, boys. When we 'build' something, we are only taking existing materials and rearranging them. All of our cutting, melting, sawing, blasting, welding, and cementing is just moving around things that already existed. Hashem did much more. He created this whole universe from nothing, from matter that did not exist before He started. He created something from nothing. A feat which humankind has not yet managed to duplicate with all of its heavy power tools and sophisticated computers."

"Please tell us, sir. Which tools did Hashem use to create this universe? He must have used unbelievably big, powerful, and sophisticated tools."

"He surely did, young man. 'Hashem said, "Let there be light," and there was light' (*Bereishis* 1:3). Hashem spoke — and the world came into being. The only tool He used was speech. Words created this universe."

"Incredible."

Kinderlach . . .
This is the might of the spoken word. Rav Yisrael Meir Kagan, known to us by the name of his famous book, Chafetz Chaim, *wrote many books about the power of the spoken word. He explains that proper speech can create worlds. When we learn Torah, pray, speak kindly, or give encouragement to people, we build up the world. Choose your words carefully, and use your speech properly. Don't you all want to be partners in this huge construction project?*

Mass Destruction

The other side of the story is also true. Words can destroy as much as they can create. The first sin in history is described in this week's parasha. We are referring to the sin of the Snake. He spoke negatively and said *lashon hara*, derogatory speech, about Hashem Himself! "For The Almighty knows that on the day that you eat of it (the fruit of the tree of knowledge) your eyes will be opened and you will be like Hashem . . . " (*Bereishis* 3:5). Rashi explains what the Snake was claiming: that Hashem did not want Adam and Chava to eat from the tree because He hated them and did not want them to gain His ability to create worlds. The Snake's malicious sin was catastrophic. It brought death to the entire world and exile from the Garden of Eden. That is the terrible destructive power of words.

Kinderlach . . .
The huge construction project can turn into a disaster if we do not watch what we say. When used improperly, speech destroys with a force unmatched by even the most powerful weapons. We all should study the books of the Chafetz Chaim and learn how to watch our words very carefully, for the gift of speech can also be a dangerous weapon.

Parashas Noach

Your Mitzvos, Your Children

"Grandpa, I always love coming to your home."

"Avi, the pleasure is all mine. You are a wonderful grandson and a joy to be with. What do you want to do today?"

"Can we look at pictures, Grandpa?"

"Of course, Avi. I have many photo albums. Which pictures would you like to see?"

"How about the ones of your father and mother. I like to see how they looked when they arrived in America, 100 years ago."

"Avi, you give me such pleasure and *nachas*. Do you know how many boys do not even want to visit their grandparents? When they do visit, they go straight to the television and all but ignore them. You are different—not only do you come to visit me, but you take the time to sit together with me and learn about our family history."

"Thank you so much, Grandpa."

"Here are the pictures of Great-Grandpa and Great-Grandma."

"Everything is so old. It looks like a different world."

"It was a different world, Avi. In many ways."

"Really? Can you tell me about it, Grandpa?"

"My pleasure, Avi. When my father arrived in America, it was very difficult for a Jew to observe Shabbos. Everyone worked six days a week and was off on Sunday. If you told your boss that you wanted to take off from work on Shabbos, he would fire you on the spot."

"What did Great-Grandpa do?"

"He got a different job every week."

"That's unbelievable."

"He would work five days and then not come on Shabbos. When he returned Monday morning, he received his pay and was told to leave."

"That must have been so difficult, Grandpa."

"It was not easy, Avi. Nevertheless, two things kept Great-Grandpa going. His love of Hashem and the mitzvos, and his love of Great-Grandma and the kids. He knew that keeping the mitzvos, and especially the Shabbos, was the most important thing in the world. He also knew that his wife and children were dependent upon him to support them. Therefore he kept the Shabbos, and he kept working."

"What a hero he was."

"True, Avi. There were many unsung heroes like him in America then. They kept the flame of Torah burning in those difficult days."

"He loved the mitzvos, and he loved his children. Was Great-Grandpa related to Rav Moshe Feinstein?"

"I don't think so. Why do you ask, Avi?"

"Because Rav Moshe writes about loving mitzvos and loving your children, in this week's parasha."

"How fascinating, Avi. Please tell me about it."

"The verse says, 'These are the offspring of Noach. Noach was a tzaddik, a righteous person, perfect in his generation' (*Bereishis* 6:9). Rashi comments that the main offspring of tzaddikim are their good deeds. The Torah could have used a different example to illustrate the point that good deeds are very important. Why did it compare them to offspring?"

"That is a good question, Avi."

"Rav Moshe explains that we should love our good deeds, our mitzvos, as we love our children. Sometimes a person takes a mitzvah lightly or does not perform it at all because he feels that it is not so important. Would he take the same attitude toward his child? Of course not! A person makes sure that his children have the very best that he can possibly give them. He should take equal care to make sure he performs his mitzvos with his very best efforts."

"Avi, that is exactly how Great-Grandpa lived his life. He took wonderful care of us, and he took great care to perform the mitzvos to the best of his abilities. Now, look at the fruits of his labors. He has merited to have a wonderful great-grandson."

"That is how Hashem rewarded him. He loved the mitzvos like he loved his children, and he merited to have children, grandchildren, and great-grandchildren who love the mitzvos just as he did."

"Avi, I am sure that at this very moment he is smiling down

upon you and all of us from Heaven."

> *Kinderlach . . .*
> *There is nothing more precious to a parent than a child. There is nothing more precious to a tzaddik than a mitzvah. So love those mitzvos as parents love their children. Hashem will reward you; He treasures those who treasure His mitzvos.*

Up The Down-Escalator

"Mommy, thank you for bringing us to this shopping mall."

"You're welcome, kinderlach. The store that we want is on the second floor. Let's go up the escalator over there."

Chani and Shoshie go up the "up" escalator. But Moishie, always the playful one, runs up the "down" escalator. He arrives at the top panting and out of breath.

"Moishie, you really came up the hard way."

"Mommy, that is what life is all about."

It is quite an accomplishment to raise our spiritual level. Noach was a tzaddik who achieved this. We may think that when we have reached a higher level we can relax and take it easy. After all, we have accomplished something truly great.

Rav Moshe Aharon Stern explains that life is like walking up a down-escalator. There is no standing still. If a person stops pressing upwards, he will slip downwards. Noach was a tzaddik who was saved while his whole generation was destroyed. He toiled without sleep for an entire year, feeding all the animals inside the ark.

When he left the ark, though, he was not pressing upwards as hard as before. He planted a vineyard, picked the grapes, made wine, and became drunk. The verse states, *"Vayachel Noach"* (*Bereishis* 9:20). Noach's spiritual level fell. Whereas before he was described as "a righteous person, perfect in his generation" (*Bereishis* 6:9), he was now called "A man of the land" (*Bereishis* 9:20). He was not going forward, therefore he went backward.

Kinderlach . . .
We are now beginning school again. Do you remember the wonderful levels we reached during the Yamim Noraim? How we cried to Hashem in our prayers? Can you still feel the intense happiness that we all felt during Succos, when we sat in the shade of Hashem's Presence? Who can forget how we danced our feet off on Simchas Torah? Now we are back to our school routines. Do not let yourselves slip down, kinderlach. Hang on to the spiritual accomplishments that you have achieved. Keep running up that down-escalator.

Parashas Lech Lecha

Let's Make a Person

"What are you doing, Chaim?"

"I'm making a chair, Avi."

"Where did you get the wood?"

"I found some scraps lying around. I am going to saw them and then screw them together. Do you want to help me, Avi?"

"It sure looks like fun, Chaim, but I have my own little construction project that I am working on."

"Really? What are you making?"

"A person."

"Come on, Avi. Let's not joke around. What are you really making?"

"I'm not joking, Chaim."

"Avi, we know that only Hashem can make a person. Unless . . . have you mastered the deep secrets of Kabbalah and learned how to make a *golem*, a man-made creature?"

"Hardly, Chaim."

"Please tell me what you are doing! I am dying of curiosity."

"I am teaching Torah to a neighbor's boy who needs some help."

"Wonderful. You are teaching him. Why did you say that you were creating him?"

"Look in this week's parasha: 'And Avram took his wife Sarai . . . and the souls they had made in Haran; and they left to go to the Land of Canaan' (*Bereishis* 12:5). Did they really create those souls in Haran? The Gemara (*Sanhedrin* 99b) relates that one who teaches Torah to his friend's son is considered as if he created him. Chaim, I am teaching Torah to my friend's son. Am I not creating him?"

"Avi, you are right. Teaching someone Torah actually forms the soul of that person, which is his essence. You are truly creating that boy. You are a real craftsman. Please let me know if any other boys need help."

"With pleasure, Chaim. The Jewish people need all the craftsmen they can find."

Kinderlach . . .
This is one of the reasons that we learn Torah. As the Mishna states (Avos 4:6), "One who learns in order to teach will have the opportunity both to learn and to teach." Learn well and understand things clearly enough so that you can teach them. You too can be a craftsman and create wonderful people.

Change the World

"And (Hashem) said to him (Avram), 'I am *El Shaddai*. Walk before me and be perfect.'" (*Bereishis* 17:1). We know that Hashem has many names. Why did He choose to refer to Himself here as "*Shaddai*"? The Malbim explains that this name is a contraction of the phrase, "I said to world, '*dai*' (enough)." Hashem created the world, and then stopped the creation at a certain point. The world was not yet finished, yet Hashem said, "*dai*." Leave the world unfinished. Man will complete the job.

The name *Shaddai* is used in conjunction with *bris mila*, circumcision. Just as the world was created incomplete, so too man is created imperfect. His first mitzvah is *mila* - perfecting his physical body. He begins his life by fixing himself, and he continues throughout his days to fix and perfect both himself and the world around him.

There is a well-known story told about the Chafetz Chaim. When he was a young boy, he wanted to change the whole world. He tried but became frustrated. Therefore, he revised his goal. He was only going to change Poland. He soon saw that also this was a bit too ambitious, so he decided to just change his little town of Radin. Alas, even this proved too much, so he decided to change just the *beis midrash*, the small synagogue where he prayed and learned. He soon realized that the only person he was capable of changing was himself. So, he got to work. As we all know, he succeeded in becoming a great Torah scholar and tzaddik. People began gravitating toward him and his *beis midrash* soon filled with people eager to learn from him. Soon his name spread beyond Radin.

The small town became a Torah center by virtue of the great tzaddik who lived there. Sure enough, the Jewish population of Poland began heeding the words of this tzaddik and *Gadol HaDor* (Torah leader). He authored important Torah books: *Mishna B'rura, Sefer Chafetz Chaim,* and many more. Anyone who wants information or inspiration on practically any aspect of Torah need only turn to him. Yes, the Chafetz Chaim succeeded. He changed the whole world.

Kinderlach . . .
You can do it. You can change the world. Where do you begin? With yourself. See yourself as whom you would want to be. Who is that big tzaddik walking down the street? It is you — 30 years from now. How do you get there? One mitzvah at a time. Wake up in a good mood. Pray well and get to school on time. Learn well and help your friends. Help Mommy when you come home. Give Daddy a warm welcome when he comes home. Go to sleep on time. Each mitzvah is another brick that builds the wall. You're building a big tzaddik. "Tzaddik yesod olam," a righteous person is the foundation of the world. Become a tzaddik. Change the world.

Parashas Vayera

Bring Out the Best in You

One day, at a top-level meeting of a successful corporation.

"Please bring me the evaluation tests of the new personnel. I want to see what job each new person is suited for."

"Yes sir, Mr. President, here they are."

"Hmmm. Let's see. Mr. Cohen scored very well in intelligence. Let's give him a thinking job. Mr. Schwartz is very good with his hands. He should be working with tools. Mr. Goldberg is very personable. He should have a job dealing with people. Mr. Levy is creative. Give him a job in the Planning Department."

"Sir, why do we take so much time and trouble with these evaluation testings?"

"This is the secret of the success of our company. Everyone gets the job for which he is suited. That way he can use his potential and develop it. The trick is to discover a person's latent talents and put him in a situation where they are needed. He will excel, which is good for him and good for the company."

"Brilliant, sir, just brilliant."

The president was not the first person to realize the value of testing a person. Hashem Himself tested our forefather Avraham many times. The Ramban, while elucidating the story of the Binding of Yitzchak (*Bereishis* 22:1), explains one of the purposes of Hashem's tests. Hashem knows the innermost thoughts, strengths, and weaknesses of a person. Therefore, He knows whether a person will pass the test or not. So why does He put a person to the test? Hashem wants the person to use his potential to do good deeds. The test turns the potential into a deed. Hashem gives reward for good deeds. Hashem tests us so that we will perform the good deeds and get the reward.

Kinderlach . . .
We are working for the World's Best Boss. He knows us inside and out. He has given us a job perfectly suited for our talents. Sometimes the job is easy, sometimes it is hard. When it gets difficult, we have to remember one thing. Our abilities are greater than we can imagine. Hashem wants us to develop to our fullest potential. Therefore, He tests us. Pass the test. Move up to the next job level. Great things await you.

The Visit That Heals

"Chaim, time to get up. You don't want to be late for school."

"Mommy, I don't feel so good today."

"Maybe you'll feel better if you get out of bed, Chaim."

"Okay Mommy. I'll try."

"Well, Chaim, do you feel any better?"

"No, Mommy. My stomach hurts, I have a headache, and I feel achy."

"You may have the flu, Chaim. Let me take your temperature."

Chaim's mother brings the thermometer.

"Yes, Chaim dear. Just as I suspected. You have 103° fever. No school for you, today. You get to stay home with Mommy all day today. We'll nurse you back to health."

"Mommy, being sick is no fun, but the best part is being with you all day."

Chaim stays in bed, sleeping most of the morning. Shortly after 3:00, the phone rings.

"Chaim, it's for you."

"Thanks, Mommy."

"Chaim, are you okay? We missed you in school today."

"Thank you so much for calling, Avi. I'm sick in bed with the flu."

"Have a *refuah shelayma* (complete recovery)."

"Thanks, Avi."
"Are you up to having a visitor?"
"That would be wonderful, Avi."
"Great. I'll be right over."

Chaim splashes some water on his face and gets himself ready for Avi's visit.
"Chaim, you look good."
"Avi, it is great to see you. It's no fun being sick."
"Chaim, the pleasure of the visit is all mine. You've given me the opportunity to do a big mitzvah."
"Is visiting sick people such a big mitzvah?"
"It certainly is. Hashem Himself performed this mitzvah."
"Really? When?"

"The very first verse in this week's parasha tells about Hashem's visit to our forefather Avraham. 'Hashem appeared to him in the plains of Mamre . . .' (*Bereishis* 18:1). Avraham was ill, recuperating from his *bris milah*. Rashi explains that Hashem came to visit the sick."
"Wow."
"Chaim, listen to what our Sages say about the mitzvah of *bikur cholim*, visiting the sick: The Gemara states that *bikur cholim* is one of the mitzvos for which a person receives reward both in this world and the next. What is that reward? Hashem will guard him from the *yetzer hara* (evil inclination), protect him from suffering, bestow honor upon him, and give him beloved friends. Visiting a sick person removes 1/60 of

the sick person's suffering. The visitor prolongs the person's life. There is no limit to the number of times that one can visit a sick person - even 100 times a day! The Divine Presence rests above the head of a sick person."

"Avi, I feel better already."

"Our Sages were so wise. They know us better than we know ourselves. Do you feel up to doing a little homework?"

"Yes, sure, Avi. Can we learn that Gemara about *bikur cholim?*"

"With pleasure, Chaim. You look 1/60 better already. We might even be privileged to see the Divine Presence here soon."

"Amen."

Kinderlach . . .

Visiting the sick is a very important mitzvah. It cheers up the sick person. That makes him feel better. Feeling better is often a big part of getting better. A person's physical state is related to his attitude. So visit a sick friend, and perk him up. He may get better sooner than you think!

Parashas Chayei Sara

Say a Little, Do a Lot

"Look at that, George. There must be twenty boxes piled up over there on the sidewalk."

"Let's see what's doing, John."

"Excuse me, sir, why are all these boxes piled up here on the sidewalk?"

"I'm sorry if I am causing any inconvenience. I run an organization that provides food for the Sabbath to needy families. I just received my weekly delivery of meat, fish, vegetables, wine, challah bread, and cake. I must get them into the storage room and then divide them up into packages for each family. Then I will distribute the packages to the families."

"That sounds like a lot of work. You wait right here. I'm going to send over some workers to help you. They will move the boxes for you, open them and divide up the contents, wrap them up into packages and even deliver the packages to the needy families. I'll send you five good strong workers and this job will be done in no time."

"Do I owe you any money for this?"

"Money? I'm giving this to you free of charge! Just wait here and the workers will be here in five minutes."

The man waits and waits. After half an hour, the workers still have not shown up.

Just then, four boys from the yeshiva walk by on their way home.

"Shalom, Rabbi Cohen."

"Shalom boys, how are you?"

"Fine. What are all those boxes, Rabbi?"

"This is food for needy families for Shabbos."

Without saying anything, each boy picks up a box.

"Where shall we put these boxes, Rabbi Cohen?"

"That's so kind of you, boys. Put them in here."

"But Rabbi, you can't leave them here. There are perishables in these boxes."

"Don't worry about it, boys, I'll take care of it."

"Rabbi Cohen, we insist. Please tell us what to do."

With that, Rabbi Cohen instructs them how to open the boxes, divide the contents, and wrap them up into packages for each of the families.

"We're all finished, Rabbi Cohen. Here are the thirty packages."

"Boys, thank you so much! I don't know where I would be without you."

"We can deliver them on our way home from yeshiva."

"Please, boys. You've done enough already. I can't ask you to do any more."

"So we'll do it without your asking, Rabbi Cohen. Please tell us the addresses."

"Are you sure it's no trouble, boys?"

"We're walking home anyway. We insist. Please Rabbi, let us finish the job."

"Okay, boys, here's the list."

"Look, these two homes are on my street."

"And those people live around the corner from me."

Within minutes, all the packages are divided among the boys. They then set out on their way to deliver them.

"Bye, boys. I don't know how to thank you. You've really saved me hours of time and hard work."

"You don't have to thank us, Rabbi Cohen. It was our pleasure."

Just that moment, the workers sent by the two men arrive.

"There is supposed to be a man with some boxes here who needs workers to help him. Do you know anything about it, sir? We were sent here to do a job for this man. We were told that he would pay us well."

"I'm sorry to disappoint you men. The work is already done."

Rabbi Cohen chuckles and thinks to himself . . .

"Things haven't changed much in the past 4000 years. The mishna in *Pirkei Avos* (1:15) states, 'Say little but do much.' Rashi explains that our forefather Avraham said very little (*Bereishis* 18:5-8). He only told his guests that he was going to serve them bread. Then he returned with butter, milk, fine tender meat, and three huge portions of flour. Efron, on the other hand, made a big promise. He offered to give Avraham the Cave of Machpela as a burial ground for Sarah, for free. In the end he demanded from Avraham an exorbitant sum of money—and received it. Rashi comments (*Bereishis* 23:16) that Efron said a lot, and did not do even a little.

"Those two men promised to take care of everything quickly, and for free. In the end, their workers showed up late, expecting to be paid. The yeshiva boys, on the other hand, came and got right to work, saying hardly anything. We see that our forefather Avraham's deeds made such a powerful impression on the Jewish people that we are still emulating them 4000 years later. When Avraham did something, he really 'did a lot.'"

Kinderlach . . .

When Mommy asks you to help her with the housework, how do you answer her? "I'll be there in a minute, Mommy." "I'll wash all the dishes, Mommy. Then I'll clean the floors. Next I'll fold the laundry." That is one way to respond.

Another way is to roll up your sleeves and get to work. Wash all of the dishes in the sink. Make the countertops shine. Sweep the dirt right off the floors. Empty the laundry basket and fill the clothes drawers with folded clothes.

Words are precious. Don't waste them. But actions speak louder than words. Say a little and do a lot.

What Did You Accomplish Today?

"And Avraham was old, he came with his days, and Hashem blessed Avraham with everything" (*Bereishis* 24:1). Where did Avraham come to, and how can you come with days? Once a day passes, it is gone. You cannot bring days with you. The Nesivos Shalom explains this verse as follows: Hashem put us into this world to grow and develop. He helps us each and every day by giving us something to accomplish. We grow by meeting these daily challenges. At the end of our lives, after 120 years, Hashem evaluates our days. Those days that we have used for growth, by performing all the mitzvos that we could, accompany us into the world to come. Those days come with us.

Kinderlach . . .

What did you accomplish today? Which challenge did Hashem set before you? Did you make peace with your brother? Did you listen to Mommy when you wanted to do something else? Did you pray well? Did you put all of your strength into learning Torah? If you made the most out of the day by doing all the mitzvos you could, then you have done Hashem's will and grown from it. You have put that day into your "spiritual savings account". That account will make you a wealthy person. Just keep making big deposits.

Parashas Toldos

The Pipeline

"Mommy, is the water okay?"

"I think so, Chaim. Why do you ask?"

"I turned the faucet on and no water came out."

"Let's see. You're right, Chaim. I wonder what's wrong?"

"Let's try another faucet. Nope. No water here either."

"What should we do, Chaim?"

"I saw Daddy look at the main water-meter once. Let's go down into the cellar and take a look."

Chaim and his mother venture down into the cellar and find water gushing out onto the floor.

Chaim alertly rushes over to the water-meter and turns off the big valve. Thankfully, the water stops.

"Mommy, let's call the plumber."

"Yes, Chaim. Here's the number."

Within half an hour, the plumber arrives at the door.

"What seems to be the problem, ma'am?"

"Come into the basement, sir."

"Looks like the main pipe has burst."

"Why was so much water gushing out, sir?"

"Son, that pipe provides all the water for all the faucets in your whole house. That's a lot of water. When it breaks, all of that water comes out. It will take me about half an hour to fix it. Then I will leave you with the mop-up work."

"Thank you so much, sir. All the water comes through one pipe. Imagine that. The builder built this house in a similar way that Hashem set up the world."

"Chaim, you certainly have a vivid imagination. How does this house resemble the world?"

"All the water comes through one pipe. What Hashem sends to the world also comes through one pipe."

"Pipe? Where is this pipe? It must be huge. I would like to go see it."

"The pipe that I am referring to is our prayers, Mommy."

"Our prayers are like a pipe?"

"A pipeline would probably be a better comparison. Hashem wants to shower this world with endless blessings. He wants to send them down from Heaven."

"What is He waiting for?"

"Us. Our prayers create the pipeline that will carry those blessings down from Heaven to earth."

"Chaim, how do you know this?"

"We learn it from this week's parasha, Mommy. Our foremother Rivkah did not have children for the first twenty years of her marriage to Yitzchak. Both Yitzchak and Rivkah poured out their hearts in prayer to Hashem. Finally, their request was granted. Rabbeinu Bechaye explains that Hashem could have given them a child right away. However, He wanted their prayers."

"Why, Chaim?"

"When we pray, Mommy, we get closer to Hashem. By constantly making requests, we come to realize that He is the One Who provides us with everything. As our relationship grows, the 'pipeline' grows wider. That allows Him to send down more blessings."

"Chaim, that is fascinating. Twenty years of praying for a child is a long time."

"Hashem never gets tired of hearing our voices. People can get annoyed if you ask too much. Hashem is happy to hear our requests because they show Him how much we appreciate Him."

"Chaim, you have added a new dimension to my prayers. I am going to try to keep this in mind when I am praying."

"Mommy, it is especially important now, when the Jewish people are facing some real dangers."

"I know, Chaim. We need a very big pipeline filled with blessings."

"May Hashem answer all of our prayers, Mommy."

"Amen."

> *Kinderlach . . .*
> *We all have things that we want and need. A good grade on the next test, a refuah shelayma (complete recovery) for the sick neighbor, a way to make peace with our little brother, a new suit for Yom Tov. These things may all be waiting to come down the pipe. We have to send in the request. Put in your order directly with The Boss. You don't need to call, fax, or even E-mail. Just open up your prayer book. He is always listening, with His Hand on the faucet.*

Who's Really Right?

The case was cut and dry. Trickery and cheating at its worst. The younger brother took advantage of his older brother's hunger, and tricked him into selling his birthright for a plate of beans. Years later, he disguised himself as his older brother, and tricked his father into giving him the special blessing reserved for the older brother. Who was right and who was wronged? The older brother looks like the innocent victim.

Rav Dessler takes a deeper look. When Eisav came to his father to get his blessing, after Yaakov had left, "Yitzchak trembled an extremely great trembling" (*Bereishis* 27:33). He sensed deceit, but who was guilty? Was it Yaakov, who disguised himself, or Yitzchak himself, who allowed himself to be misled? As the verse states, "The voice is Yaakov's voice, but the hands are Eisav's hands" (27:22). Hashem assured Yitzchak that neither of them was guilty. Eisav, "the hunter with his mouth" (25:28), was the trickster. He trapped the game with his nets, and he deceived his father with his mouth. He appeared to be very righteous on the outside, asking Yitzchak how to be strict in performance of mitzvos. Does one need to give *maaser* (tithes) from salt? Yet inside, he was immoral and corrupt. Yaakov and Yitzchak corrected the situation by switching the blessings. They were really right.

Kinderlach . . .

We learn two very important lessons from this episode. Things are not always as they appear. The one who looks right may actually be wrong. The one who looks wrong may actually be right. We have to judge people and situations very carefully. Consult with older and wiser people before you come to conclusions.

*Secondly, we have to be truly good. "If I close my eyes while I pray and look like I am really concentrating, then people will think that I am praying well." The mitzvah is to **have** true concentration, not to put on a show. Looks are not enough. They are only skin deep. Kinderlach, put Hashem deep in your hearts. Then you will be truly good people, inside and out.*

Parashas Vayetze

A Dream Ending

"That tree looks very strong and healthy, Daddy."

"That is because is has good, solid roots, Chaim. Those other weak trees were not planted and watered properly. Their roots never had a chance to develop, and that's why the trees suffered."

The Malbim relates that our holy Forefathers are the "roots" of our nation. The events that they experienced guide our lives, just as the roots guide the development of the tree.

"And Yaakov left Beer Sheva" (Bereishis 28:10). Thus began his personal exile, which is a parable for our current exile. "He spent the night there because the sun had set" (28:11). The exile is like a long night. The cause of the exile is *sinas chinam*, unjustified hatred. Redemption will come when we unite. Just as Yaakov's stones, which he had placed around his head to protect him while sleeping, united and formed one stone. Upon these united stones, Yaakov fell asleep and dreamed his famous dream about a ladder connecting heaven and earth, with angels ascending and descending. This dream hints to the future Temple, which will unite heaven and earth.

> *Kinderlach . . .*
> *King David writes, "When Hashem will return the captives of Zion we will be like dreamers" (Tehillim 126). This long, bitter exile will be like a dream. We want to wake up from that dream. It is in our hands. Replace the* sinas chinam *with* ahavas chinam, *unconditional love. Unite with all Jews and feel at one with them. Connect heaven and earth. Give this story a dream ending.*

The Well

"Daddy, where did our forefather Yaakov meet his wife Rachel?"

"By the well."

"And where did Eliezer meet Rivkah, who became Yitzchak's wife?"

"By the well."

"And where did Moshe Rabbeinu meet his wife Tzipporah?"

"By the well."

"Well, well, well. They all met by the well. What's so special about the well?"

"Excellent question, Avi. The Malbim has a beautiful explanation that shows you how deep the well really is."

"Daddy, you are so poetic."

"Our sages relate a story about a well. An elderly sage asked Rabbi Yehoshua how to bring a well from the field into the city. He answered, 'Bind it with ropes made of bran, and bring it in.'"

"That is a strange question and answer, Daddy. It needs explanation."

"Yes, Avi. The question and answer are really a parable. All of the good that Hashem bestows on this world is called *'beer mayim chaim'* (the well of living waters). He is The Source of all good, just as water is the source of all life. When the Jewish people are in their homeland, in the Land of Israel, the parable relates that the well is in the city. When we are in exile and the Divine Presence is in exile with us, then the well is in the field. When the elderly sage asked about bringing the well into the city, he was really asking about ending the exile and bringing the Jews back to the Holy Land."

"That is a question that we all want to know the answer to, Daddy."

"Bind the well with ropes made of bran, and bring it in."

"Daddy, you can't make ropes from bran. It does not stick together."

"Exactly, Avi. Our exile is due to *sinas chinam*, hatred for an unjustified reason. The Jewish people when afflicted by *sinas chinam* are compared to bran, which cannot stick together. We do not love each other enough to stick together."

"What can we do to correct that, Daddy?"

"The verse continues by saying that three flocks of sheep drank from the well. The sheep are the Jewish people, whose whole existence is from Hashem's goodness. There is only one problem. There was a big stone on the well, which could only be moved by all of the shepherds together. The big stone is compared to the *yetzer hara*, the evil inclination, and the sins he causes, which block us from receiving Hashem's bounty. When all of the shepherds gathered together, they were able to remove the stone and open the well. So too, when all of the Jewish people gather together, we can open the well."

"But Daddy, the shepherds returned the stone to the well after every time they watered their sheep."

"You are very smart, Avi. We have returned to exile many times, even after we have done *t'shuva* and repented our sins. However, while the stone was on the well, Rachel came to the well with her sheep. Yaakov then took the stone off the well all by himself. In Yaakov's merit the final redemption will come, when Rachel comes to the well with her holy sheep, the flocks of Jewish people who thirst for Hashem's blessings."

Kinderlach . . .
We are all anxiously awaiting the coming of Mashiach. Unity is the key to ending this exile. How do we increase unity? Be nice to people. They will be drawn to you. Do not begin or continue senseless arguments. Compromise and make peace at every opportunity. Love your fellow Jews. Bring the well home.

Parashas Vayishlach

The Home

"Mommy, I'm home."

"Shalom, Devora! Welcome home. How was school?"

"Wonderful, Mommy."

"Take off your coat and let me give you a big hug."

"Mommy, you're the best. What's that delicious smell?"

"Vegetable soup. I have a nice hot lunch for you."

"Yum. I'm so hungry."

"Okay, go wash and sit down so we can eat together."

"Mommy, it's so nice to eat with you every day."

"It's my pleasure, Devora."

"Mommy, can I tell you something personal?"

"Of course, my dear."

"You work so hard to make our home nice. You greet us with a smile, a hug, and a kiss. You always try to have a warm meal waiting for us. You take care of all of us. You toil to make our home clean, orderly, and well stocked with food. You make time to listen to us, and to give us good advice. You make Shabbos and Yomim Tovim so beautiful and special. I just love coming home!"

"Devora dear, you make me feel so good. I work so hard on all of these things. It is wonderful to hear your appreciation. Can I tell you a secret?"

"Sure, Mommy."

"This is the most important thing that I can be doing."

"Why, Mommy?"

"What is the most precious thing in the world?"

"Gold? Diamonds?"

"No."

"What, Mommy?"

"People. Do you know what people can accomplish? People can move mountains. They can create cities. They can write beautiful Torah thoughts. But an evil person can destroy a whole world. People are worth more than anything."

"What's the secret that you wanted to tell me, Mommy?"

"Do you see those two house plants over there, Devora?"

"Yes, Mommy. One looks very strong and healthy. But the other one is barely alive."

"When I bought them, they looked the same. I planted one in a flowerpot filled with good, rich soil. It grew big, strong, and beautiful. The other one was planted in weak soil. It hardly grew at all."

"Mommy, tell me the secret."

"A person is like a plant, and a home is like the soil in the pot. When a person grows up in a good home, he will flourish. His body and soul will receive the nourishment that they need to bloom into a healthy, strong, productive adult. If

not, the person will find it much more difficult to meet life's challenges. That is why my work in the home is so important. It helps to make you into beautiful people. This is the secret of the most precious thing in the world."

"Mommy, how do you know all of this?"

"We have a hint in this week's parasha. The Torah writes that Dinah, the daughter of Leah, went out to see the daughters of the land where they were living (Bereishis 34:1). Unfortunately, a terrible thing happened to her when she went out. The Midrash Tanchuma comments on this event by quoting a verse in Tehillim (45:14), 'All of the honor of a princess is inside.' When a woman is modest within her home, she atones for her family members. A modest woman becomes like a fruitful vine. Her children become like strong olive trees."

"Mommy, that is beautiful."

"The home is the woman's field of endeavor. That is where she can be creative. That is where she can create life's most valuable possessions."

Kinderlach . . .

Beautiful daughters, we are counting upon you. You are our future. You create the next generation. You make the home that nurtures them into beautiful people. Where would we be without people? Nowhere. Where would we be without you? Nowhere. We appreciate you!

Honoring Parents

After thirty-four years of separation, Yaakov is on his way to meet his brother Eisav. He is informed that Eisav is coming to meet him with 400 men at his side. "And Yaakov was very frightened . . ." (Bereishis 32:8). Why? Yaakov certainly had faith and trust in Hashem. He also had the merit of many mitzvos to protect him. He had learned Torah with Shem and Ever for fourteen years. He observed all 613 mitzvos in the house of Lavan. But what about Eisav?

The Midrash explains that Eisav also had mitzvos to his merit. "All of these years Eisav honored his parents. He will come to battle me with the strength of that mitzvah on his side." For those thirty-four years, Eisav honored his parents and Yaakov did not. Even with all of his merits, Yaakov was still afraid of Eisav because he had honored his parents. This shows the importance of honoring our parents.

Kinderlach . . .
Honoring Daddy and Mommy is one of the mitzvos whose reward is spelled out in the Torah. "Honor your father and mother so that your days will be lengthened" (Shemos 20:12). We honor them by helping them and serving them. And we revere them by standing up for them, listening to them, and not contradicting them. By honoring our parents we are really honoring Hashem. Let us all do our best to strengthen our observance of this very important mitzvah.

Parashas Vayeshev

Blockbuster

One day at the office of the top executive of a big movie studio.

"Jones, bring me the ticket sales report."

"Here it is, R. J."

"This is terrible. Our ticket sales are way down. What is the reason for this?"

"Everyone is going to see the new blockbuster adventure movie put out by the other studio. It is the biggest box seller in history."

"Rats! We need a movie like that! Do we have any new scripts to look at?"

"A few arrived in the mail today."

"Please bring them to me. Let's open them and have a look."

The two men open the mail and begin reading the scripts.

"Listen to this, R. J. This one sounds very interesting. It is a real adventure story."

"Go ahead and read it to me, Jones."

"The first scene opens as the father of a large family

presents one of his youngest sons with a special gift. The son, seventeen years old, is happy to receive a special unique coat, presented just to him and not to his older brothers. His brothers are upset. This coat is just another act of favoritism toward the younger son.

"Scene two begins with the ten older brothers tending their sheep in the pastures. Their young brother approaches, wearing his special coat.
'Now is our chance to get even. Let's kill him.'
'We can't kill our own brother. Let's throw him into a pit. Someone or something else will take care of him.'
"With that, the brothers rip off his coat and throw him into the pit. The pit is full of snakes and scorpions, but miraculously, they do not bite the young son. The brothers sit down to eat.
'Look, what is that off in the distance? It looks like a caravan of traders. Why should we leave our brother in the pit to die? Let us sell him to the traders.'
"The brothers return to the pit, draw their brother out, and sell him to some traders who in turn sell him as a slave to the Bedouins."

"I like it, Jones. Sounds good. Those miraculous snakes and scorpions are a little far-fetched, but the script has potential. Keep reading."
"Scene three: The Bedouins arrive in Egypt, with their young slave. They sell him to one of the officers of Pharaoh,

the king of Egypt. The officer brings him home to be a servant in his house. Something incredible begins to happen. This lowly slave begins to show great expertise in running the home of the king's officer. His master gives him more and more responsibility, and sees more and more profit and success in the doings of his household. The officer soon puts the slave in charge of his whole household. The slave's brilliant management makes the officer a very wealthy man."

"Jones, this story is almost a fantasy. How can a young slave become a brilliant business manager overnight? Still, the plot is fast-paced. Let's keep going."

"Scene four: The officer's wife casts her eyes on the youthful slave and makes demands of him. He refuses. How can he betray his master who trusts him with the whole household? The wife becomes angry and reports to her husband that the slave has betrayed him. With that, the master throws the slave into prison."

"I guess our hero slave is finished, Jones. Nobody ever escapes from prison, let alone a slave."
"This is getting exciting, R. J."
"You're right, Jones. Read on."

"Scene five: The prison warden notices that the young slave has special talents. He puts him in charge of some of the inmates. The young slave is successful, just as he was in the home of the officer. Before long, the warden hands over the whole operation of the prison to the young slave."

"This slave is a real phenomenon, R. J. Can you imagine how he would do on Wall Street?"

"Keep reading, Jones."

"Scene six: The king throws two of his officers into prison for neglecting their duties. There in prison, they meet the young slave. They each have a strange dream on the same night. The next morning they discuss the dreams with the young slave. He interprets their dreams and foretells that one officer will be executed and one will return to his post. 'Please remember me,' he says to the officer who will return to his post."

"Come on, Jones, what king puts an officer in prison and then takes him out? Is this a joke? Prison is serious business."

"Do you want me to stop reading, R. J.?"

"No, of course not. This can be the blockbuster that we need."

"Scene seven: Two years later, Pharaoh king of Egypt has a very strange dream which no one can make sense of. Only then does the officer remember the young slave in the prison. 'Your Majesty, there was a slave in the prison who interpreted my dream, and it came true just as he said.' 'Bring him to me,' commanded the king. The young slave shaves, changes his clothes, and is brought before the king.

"The young slave interprets the dream without hesitation: 'Your Majesty's dream foretells seven years of plenty, followed by seven years of famine in the land of Egypt. Let Your Majesty appoint an officer to gather grain during the years of plenty. Then Your Majesty will have food supplies during the famine years.' The king then does an unbelievable thing. He appoints the lowly slave to the position of second in command of all of Egypt. He and only he will be in charge of gathering all of the grain during the years of plenty, and selling it during the famine."

"Jones, this is not an adventure story. This is a fantasy. No one would ever believe this. A slave becoming second-in-command to the king? Impossible. Who is the author of this story? Get him on the telephone. Tell him that the plot is basically good, but a few changes must be made to make it a little more believable."

"R. J., you had better sit down. We will not be able to contact the author or change the plot."
"WHAT !!! Who is he? What is his price? Everybody has his price."
"R. J., this story is from the Bible. It is the story of Joseph. The author is Hashem, and the story is true."

R. J. sits down and takes a few deep breaths. He thinks for a few minutes and begins to speak.

"Jones, I had a suspicion that this was too good to be true. The truth is always stranger than fiction. Come, let's read the original story in the Bible. That will put everything back into proportion. None of our petty screenplays and films can match the blockbuster world that Hashem has created."

Kinderlach . . .

Hashem included many stories in the Torah to teach us many things. Hashem gave us a special treat, by making these stories very interesting. Some people read fictional stories to relax and escape. Authors are gifted with the creativity to write captivating tales. But we all know that the best stories are the true ones. Why? Because Hashem is a better storywriter than any of us. The lives of our holy Forefathers are filled with real suspense. These are true events which teach us the principles of emunah. *Read them, enjoy them, and learn from them.*

Remember something else, kinderlach. Just as Hashem wrote the story of their lives, He is writing the story of our lives. Pay attention to real life. Your own life. You are living Hashem's script. It is much more exciting and interesting than any novel you can ever read. And it is also filled with lessons of emunah.

Parashas Miketz

Turnaround

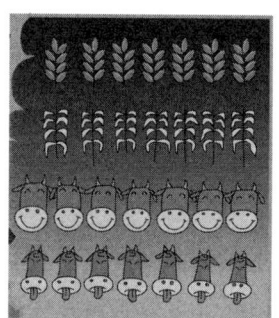

"Hi, Avi, how was school today?"
"I am so upset, Daddy."
"Why?"
"The teacher changed a few seats around in class. I am now sitting next to a boy who doesn't pay attention at all during class. I am afraid that he will ruin my behavior completely."

"That's understandable. Did you speak to the teacher about it?"

"I did. He said that the boy must sit next to someone. He picked me because my behavior is so good that he thinks that I can have an influence on the boy."

"Wow! That must have made you feel great, Avi."

"Yes and no. I am happy that he thinks so highly of me, but worried that the boy will influence me more than I will influence him."

"Avi, let me speak with the teacher, and then we will talk about what he said."

"Sure, Daddy."

Avi's father calls up the teacher and speaks for quite a long time. At the end of the conversation, he calls Avi into the room.

"Avi, I want to tell you what the teacher said, but first I would like to tell you a story."

"Great, Daddy."

"One time, when I was a little older than you, I was looking for a study partner to learn Gemara. I was fortunate enough to get the best boy in the class as my study partner. I came home from school that day flying. I was so happy. I was looking forward to a great year of learning Gemara with that boy. The next day I got to school and I sat down next to him, ready to learn. He said that he was sorry but he had to make a change of plans. A family member had just arrived from out of town and he had to learn with that boy. Family obligations came first. I understood completely. I knew the importance of family. Since it was only the first day of school, it would be easy for me to find someone else to learn with. But I could not help feeling disappointed. I felt that things were not working out for the best."

"What happened, Daddy? Did you find another study partner?"

"I surely did. He was not as brilliant as the first boy was, but he plugged away at his learning. He had a great influence on me in two ways. First, he taught me to be a plugger. Secondly, I had to do most of the explaining when we learned together. This taught me how to explain things very clearly, which helped my learning tremendously."

"What you're trying to tell me, Daddy, is that it looked bad in the beginning but turned out good in the end."

"Exactly, Avi. Can you think of an example from the Torah of something like this?"

"Hmmm. I know! Yosef HaTzaddik!"

"Right! What happened with Yosef?"

"His brothers sold him as a slave to a band of travelers. They thought that he would just be a lowly slave the rest of his life and they would never see him again. Imagine their astonishment when they met up with him again, over twenty years later, and he was not the lowly slave that they had sold but none other than the second in command of all of Egypt, the most powerful country in the world! He forgave them for what they did, and explained that it was part of Hashem's plan that he had ended up there. For he was now able to feed them and the whole world during the years of famine."

"I see you know the story really well, Avi."

"It really proves your point, Daddy. We may think that something is bad, but in the end, it turns out to be the best thing for us."

"Exactly, Avi. Your teacher explained to me that he has real confidence in you. He feels that you are able to have an influence on this boy. The boy does not behave negatively. He just needs to learn how to work a little harder, something he could pick up from your good example. This is a real opportunity for you, Avi."

"You are so right, Daddy. I am going to turn around my way of thinking from negative to positive."

"Avi, if you keep up the good work, you are truly going to turn around the situation. You can even turn around this boy's whole life."

> *Kinderlach . . .*
> *Things are not always as they seem. Something may look bad to us, when in fact it is very good. "Daddy, I got a low grade in the test." "That's just a sign that you have to work harder, Chaim. No one ever accomplished anything worthwhile without hard work. You should thank the teacher for showing you where you need to improve." Brighten your world. See the positive in everything.*

He's Paying Attention

"Just remember me . . . " (Bereishis 40:14). Yosef HaTzaddik paid dearly for those words. Yosef and the Royal Cupbearer were in prison together. Yosef interpreted this officer's strange dream to mean that in three days he would be released and restored to his royal position. Yosef requested that he then ask Pharaoh to release him from this prison. Because Yosef placed his faith in the officer, and not in Hashem, Yosef stayed an additional two years in prison.

What actually happened? "The Royal Cupbearer did not remember Yosef, rather he forgot him" (Bereishis 40:23). The

K'li Yakar explains that this is the way of the world. One who feels that he is important forgets those whom he feels are beneath him. However, Hashem's ways are different. He is greater than all of Creation, yet He remembers each one of us, and our deeds. This is a sign of His great humility.

"It happened at the end of two years, to the day" (Bereishis 41:1). Rabbeinu Bechaye relates that the word *miketz* comes from the root word *ketz*, which means "end." It also can mean "fixed amount." Each and every decree that comes from Hashem's mouth is exact. On Rosh Hashanah, He evaluates all of our accomplishments of the past year, and then fixes our finances, health, and overall physical state for the next year. Precisely. That is what He did with Yosef. His punishment was to stay exactly two extra years in prison. To the day. The very next night, Pharaoh dreamed his dream.

Kinderlach . . .
We learn two very important things from these events. Hashem is paying attention to everything that you do. Doesn't that make you feel important? He takes note of everything, remembers it, and evaluates it. Then He arranges the events of your life. The things that happen are tailor-made exactly for you. That should make you feel even more important. The King of all kings is paying close attention to you, and helping you by guiding your life every step of the way. What could be better than that?

Parashas Vayigash

The Right Address

"Chaim, can you please do an errand for me?"

"Sure thing, Mommy. What would you like?"

"Can you please go to the store and buy a dozen eggs? Here is the money."

"I'll be back in a jiffy, Mommy."

Chaim takes the money and runs down the street, anxious to do the mitzvah of helping his mother. He gets to the store, enters, and looks around.

"Excuse me sir, I would like to buy something, but I do not see it on the shelves..."

"What would you like, young man?"

"A dozen eggs."

"Young man, this is a hardware store. We do not sell eggs here."

"I did not realize that, sir. Sorry for troubling you."

Chaim moves on to the next store, opens the door, walks

in, and approaches the first saleswoman.

"May I help you, young man?"

"Yes. I need to buy something for my mother."

"What do you need, young man. We have all types of ladies' clothing here."

"She sent me to buy a dozen eggs."

"You are not going to find eggs in a clothing store, young man."

"I guess I am in the wrong store. Sorry."

Chaim is undaunted. He wants to help his Mommy. The next store is just up the street. He is sure that he will find what he needs in here.

"Young man, you look like you are anxious to buy something."

"I sure am, sir. I want to buy a dozen eggs for my mother."

"Young man, this is a stationary store. We only sell paper goods here."

Chaim looks so disappointed. He wants so badly to help his Mommy.

"Young man, you look so sad. What is the matter?"

"This is the third store that I've been to, and none of them sell eggs. Isn't there one address where I can get everything? Then I won't have to go looking around from place to place."

The storekeeper strokes his beard and smiles warmly at Chaim. This is an opportunity to make a Kiddush Hashem

(Sanctification of Hashem's Name). He takes a prayer book off the shelf and opens to the Sh'moneh Esrei *of the daily prayers.*

"Young man, here is the address for everything."

"I don't understand, sir. This is a *siddur,* not an address book."

"Young man, the Jewish people say these prayers to Hashem three times every day. We ask Him for wisdom, forgiveness, health, livelihood, reward, justice, peace, as well as many other things. Now tell me something, young man. Would you ask someone for something, knowing that he could not give it to you?"

"No sir. That would be a waste of time."

"We ask Hashem for all of these things. Is He capable of giving them to us?"

"Of course. Why else would we ask Him?"

"Then He is the address that you have been looking for. He is the One who can provide you with everything. And He wants to give it to you."

"What do I have to do?"

"First of all, you have to ask, ask, and ask again. This is not being an annoying nudnik to Hashem. He *wants* you to keep asking. Then you will realize that everything comes from Him. Our forefather Yaakov took the time to offer sacrifices and pray to Hashem when he was on his way down to Egypt to meet his son Yosef (*Bereishis* 46:1). He was concerned about what would happen to the Jewish people when they left the

Land of Israel."

"He knew the right address."

"That's right. And now you know it too."

> *Kinderlach . . .*
> *There is one address for all of your requests. Hashem. Three times a day. Are you feeling sick? Ask Him for good health. Do you want to do well on your Chumash test? He can help you. Are you having a hard time getting along with your brother? Hashem is the peacemaker. He wants you to ask Him for everything. Soon it will begin to dawn on you that He is the One Who provides us with everything that we have. Then you will realize how wonderful He is. And you will want to be close to Him. Kinderlach, that is the best thing in the world.*

Gratitude

The air was charged with anticipation. The emotion-packed reunion between Yaakov and his long-lost son Yosef was about to take place (*Bereishis* 46:29). We can imagine the feelings our forefather Yaakov had for his favorite son. He loved him so much that he refused to be consoled the entire time that Yosef was gone. Yaakov was a *navi*, a prophet. A *navi* can only receive prophecy from Hashem when he is happy. Yaakov did not have one prophecy during the entire time of Yosef's absence, due to his extreme sadness.

We can only begin to picture how happy he must have been to see Yosef.

What actually happened? Yosef fell onto Yaakov's neck and wept. Rashi explains that Yaakov, however, did not weep. Instead he recited the Shema, the prayer by which we accept *Ol Malchus Shamayim,* the Yoke of Heaven, upon ourselves. At the height of his ecstasy over seeing Yosef, his first thought was of Hashem.

When Yaakov saw his son Yosef, love and fear of Hashem came into his heart. The Maharal in his work *Gur Aryeh* relates that this is the trait of *tzaddikim:* when something good happens to them, they cleave to Hashem because of the kindness and truth that He has done for them.

Kinderlach . . .
What was Yaakov's first thought when something good happened to him? To thank and praise Hashem. This gratitude, hakaras hatov, *is a wonderful trait that we can learn. What do we do when good things happen to us? Do we say, "Baruch Hashem?" "Thank God"? We should. We know that all good things come from Hashem, so why not go ahead and thank Him? The next time we get a good grade on a test, let's say, "Baruch Hashem!" When our grandparents come to visit us from far away, let's say "Baruch Hashem!" We're so happy that Hashem has been good to us!*

Forgive and Live

"He (Yosef) kissed all of his brothers and wept upon them" (*Bereishis* 45:15). The Sh'lah comments, "See how much a person needs to forgive and let things pass. They sinned against Yosef, and Yosef cried and kissed them." The Sefer HaChinuch (Mitzvah 241 - "do not take revenge", and Mitzvah 242 - "do not bear a grudge") explains as follows: When one person wrongs another, it is natural to look for an opportunity to get back at the other person. The Torah comes along and says, "Do not take revenge. Do not bear a grudge." (*Vayikra* 19:18). How can we accomplish this? By realizing that everything that happens to us, good or bad, is from Hashem. Nothing can happen against His will. Yosef himself tells the brothers this: "It was not you who sent me here, but Hashem." (*Bereishis* 45:8).

Kinderlach . . .
"Chani still has not returned the book that she borrowed from me. It is five days overdue. The next time she wants something, she can go borrow it somewhere else." Kinderlach, we have to try very hard to judge Chani favorably. She probably forgot about the book—after all, she is usually so responsible. Hashem is sending us this test. We must learn to forgive and not take revenge. This is a very valuable lesson, and now is the time to learn it. If we learn to judge people favorably and forgive them, we will save ourselves so much distress and aggravation later in life. Learning to forgive is learning how to live.

Parashas Vayechi

A Good Education

ישמך
אלקים
כאפרים
וכמנשה

"Good Shabbos, everyone!"
"Good Shabbos, Daddy!"
"Everyone looks so nice in their Shabbos clothes. Your eyes are all sparkling with the light of the Shabbos candles."
"Yours are also, Daddy."
"Thank you. Come to get your *brochos* (blessings). Chaim, you're first because you are the oldest. *Yesimcha Elokim Ki-Efraim Vi-Ki-Menashe* (May God make you like Efraim and like Menashe)."

"Daddy, can I ask you a question?"
"Sure. Go ahead, Chaim."
"This was the blessing that our forefather Yaakov gave to his grandsons, correct?"
"Yes."
"And this is the blessing that all fathers were commanded to bless their sons with, correct?"
"The verse says, 'this is how Israel (the Jewish people) shall bless.'"
"Daddy, Yaakov had many sons. Why don't we bless our

children with one of the blessings that he gave to his sons? Why do we bless our sons with the blessing of Efraim and Menashe, who weren't even his sons?"

"Chaim, that is an excellent question. The Torah leader of the previous generation, Rav Moshe Feinstein, also asked that question."

"How did he answer it?"

"The Torah (*Shemos* 48:5) writes that Efraim and Menashe, although they were born in Egypt, were like sons to their grandfather Yaakov. The other grandsons were born in the Land of Israel and were raised close to Yaakov. They should have been considered his sons. What was so special about Efraim and Menashe? The Torah is telling us that a father must educate his children very well in Torah and mitzvos. So well that the child will follow the Torah under even the most difficult circumstances. Yaakov's son Yosef, the father of Efraim and Menashe, kept the entire Torah always: while he was a slave, while he was in prison, and while he was in the royal court of Pharaoh. None of his family was there to help him. Not only that, he educated his sons, Efraim and Menashe, to learn Torah and keep mitzvos, even in these alien surroundings."

"That's amazing, Daddy."

"Do you see what a wonderful education Yosef received?"

"The best."

Kinderlach . . .
This is what Daddy and Mommy are trying to accomplish. Sometimes they are strict with you. Sometimes it is not easy to listen to what they say. You may think it is not fair. However, Hashem made them your parents, and they have a mitzvah to educate you. They are doing their very best. When they give you the blessing on Shabbos evening, think about how much they love you, and how much they want you to be a tzaddik, just like Efraim and Menashe.

Give Him Honor

"Leah, did you get your *Chumash* test back?"

"Yes I did, Miri."

"Do you mind if I ask you how you did on the test?"

"I don't mind at all, Miri. I got a 95."

"Ninety-five! That's great, Leah. You are so smart."

"Baruch Hashem."

"You always say that when I compliment you, Leah."

"Say what?"

"'Baruch Hashem.' Why do you say it?"

"My parents say it. They are wonderful role models. I always try to do what they do. Now you've got my curiosity going, though. I want to ask them why they always say 'Baruch Hashem.'"

"When you find out, please tell me."

"Sure, Miri."

A few minutes later . . .

"Mommy, I'm home."

"Great to see you, Leah. How was school today?"

"Great. I got a 95 in my *Chumash* test."

"Baruch Hashem."

"I'm glad that you said that, Mommy."

"So am I."

"I always wanted to know why you say 'Baruch Hashem' whenever you hear good news, or whenever someone gives you a compliment."

"Leah, you always ask the most thoughtful questions."

"Baruch Hashem."

"A compliment is a very nice thing. It tells a person about his good qualities. Think about it for a minute: who gave the person his talents?"

"Hashem."

"Who gave him the opportunities to develop his good qualities?"

"Hashem."

"Who keeps a person alive every minute of every day?"

"Hashem."

"Therefore, who deserves to be blessed when a person does something good?"

"Hashem."

"Right. That is why we say Baruch Hashem. Do you know one of the sources of this in the Torah, Leah?"

"Let me guess -- this week's parasha."

"Right, Leah. Our forefather Yaakov was sick in bed at the end of his life. Yosef brought his two sons before him, Efraim and Menashe, to receive a blessing. Yaakov asked Yosef, 'Who are they?' Yosef replied, 'These are my sons who Hashem has given to me here' (*Bereishis* 48:8-9). The Ohr HaChaim HaKadosh comments that the way of righteous people, whenever they mention a good thing that happened to them, is that they give honor to Hashem. For He is the Giver. That is what we are doing when we say, 'Baruch Hashem.' We are giving all of the credit to Him."

"Mommy, I have only one thing to say."

"What, Leah?"

"Baruch Hashem."

Kinderlach . . .

Did someone give you a compliment today? Baruch Hashem. "Esti, you got dressed so quickly this morning." "Baruch Hashem." "Ahuva, you washed the floors of the whole house." "Baruch Hashem." "Grandma, you brought us such yummy treats for Shabbos." "Baruch Hashem." "Shoshie, you made peace with the neighbor." "Baruch Hashem." "Mommy, the Shabbos food is outstanding." "Baruch Hashem." This is how we respond to good things, good news, and compliments. We give honor to the One Who made these good things happen.

Tell Them You Love Them

"Then Yisrael saw Yosef's sons and he said, 'Who are these?' And Yosef said to his father, 'They are my sons whom Hashem has given me here'" (*Bereishis* 48:8-9). Why did Yisrael ask this question? He surely knew who Menashe and Efraim were. After all, he taught them Torah for seventeen years while he was in Egypt.

The Ohr HaChaim HaKadosh answers this question in a lovely way. Yisrael was about to bless his grandchildren. Before the blessing, he wanted to arouse his love for them. This would enhance the blessing because it would be coming at a time of great love and affection. So he asked his dear son Yosef who they were. Now he would hear the words coming from Yosef's mouth, "They are my sons." His heart would open up to them and he would bless them with the love of a parent for his offspring.

This is the hidden meaning of the verse, "Is Efraim My favorite son or a delightful child, that whenever I speak of him I remember him more and more?" (*Yirmiahu* 31:19). Speaking about him arouses Hashem's love for him.

Kinderlach . . .
We know that we are supposed to love our fellow Jews, especially close family members, but we sometimes need help. The Ohr HaChaim HaKadosh gives us a valuable insight. Speak about them. Tell your parents how much you appreciate them. You will feel the warm feeling of true love glowing in your heart. Tell your sister that you love her. Watch her face light up, and feel your love for her grow. Hashem gave us beautiful emotions. Learn how to use them in the proper time and place. Love your fellow Jews

Simcha's Kinder Torah

Sefer Shemos

Holy Ground

"Tzippy, please come in to the house now."

"Mommy, we're playing jump rope and my turn is next. Can I take my turn and then come in?"

"How long will that be Tzippy?"

"Five minutes."

"Okay. See you in five minutes."

"Thank you Mommy."

Five minutes later . . .

"Here I am Mommy."

"Tzippy, thank you for being so prompt. Now it is time to do your homework. We are going to eat in about an hour, and you have to take a bath tonight, so you must begin your homework now."

"Mommy, my tummy hurts, and I have a headache, and I'm tired from playing jump rope. I don't feel like doing homework now."

"Tzippy, when you were jumping around outside, you didn't complain about your tummy and your head."

"I guess I wasn't thinking about them."

"It doesn't matter. Once you begin your homework, you

won't be thinking about them either. Now take a drink of water and see if you feel better."

"Okay Mommy. Can you help me with my homework?"

"Sure, Tzippy. What is it about?"

"Moshe Rabbeinu."

"I'll try. What is the question?"

"We have to write a word of Torah about Moshe Rabbeinu, from this week's parasha."

"How about the burning bush?"

"That's a great idea, Mommy. How does the story go again?"

"Moshe Rabbeinu was tending sheep in the land of Midian. He saw a bush that was burning. However, there was something very strange about that bush. It kept burning and burning and burning."

"And it never got burned up."

"Right."

"Moshe Rabbeinu turned aside to get a good look at this bush, because it was a wondrous site. Then Hashem called out to him from the bush. Do you remember what He said, Tzippy?"

"Something about shoes?"

"Right again! 'Take your shoes off your feet, because the place where you are standing is holy ground.'"

"Where was Moshe standing, Mommy? In the place of the Holy Temple?"

"No."

"In the Holy City of Jerusalem?"

"No."

"In the Holy Land of Israel?"

"No."

"Then what was so holy about that place?"

"Excellent question, Tzippy. The Chafetz Chaim asks the very same question."

"That's really exciting. What's the answer?"

"Every place where you are standing is holy ground."

"How can that be?"

"Because, my dear Tzippy, you have the opportunity to make it holy."

"Wow. How, Mommy?"

"When Hashem gives you a mitzvah to do, it is an opportunity to make that moment and place in your life holy. That is the purpose of a mitzvah. To turn ordinary things into holy things. When you give charity, you make ordinary money holy. Did you ever write a nice note to someone and make them feel good?"

"Sure, Mommy."

"You have taken an ordinary piece of paper and some ink, and turned it into a wonderful note which brightens a person's whole day. What a mitzvah!"

"That's great, Mommy, but I still don't understand what the Chafetz Chaim is saying about the burning bush."

"Hashem was pointing out this fact to Moshe Rabbeinu. By telling him to take off his shoes because this ground was holy, He was telling Moshe that all ground is truly holy. We just do not see the holiness. Sometimes, a mitzvah is difficult for us to do. We're tired. We're hungry. We have a headache. We would rather just forget the whole thing. Why? Because we do not see the holiness. That mitzvah is holy ground and we do not realize it."

"I am beginning to understand, Mommy. When you told me to begin my homework, that was an opportunity to do the mitzvah of listening to you, and to learn Torah at the same time."

"Excellent, Tzippy! Now let me tell you something else. Sometime it is easy to do a mitzvah. Other times, that same mitzvah is difficult because you are tired or hungry. The reward for a mitzvah when it is difficult is much greater than the reward for that same mitzvah when it is easy to do."

"Wow."

"Sometimes we try to avoid mitzvos when they are difficult. We do not realize that we are on holy ground. Hashem had a good reason to give us this mitzvah now when it is difficult. He wanted us to get a bigger reward."

"That's great, Mommy. What a great word of Torah. Thank you so much for helping me with my homework. I'm going to write it down now."

"Fantastic, Tzippy."

"Do you know something, Mommy? You were right. My tummy doesn't hurt anymore. And I don't have a headache. And I'm not tired."

"Baruch Hashem."

"I guess I just did not realize where I was."

"Where were you, Tzippy?"

"On holy ground."

Kinderlach . . .
Everywhere is holy ground. Hashem presents us with mitzvos all of the time. Did you listen to Mommy without interrupting? You got a mitzvah. Did you make a blessing before you ate the apple? You got a mitzvah. Did you let your brother have the last piece of cake? You got a mitzvah. Did you learn Torah? You got a mitzvah. Did you smile and make someone feel good? You got a mitzvah. The world is full of mitzvos, each one a holy opportunity. Don't let them slip by.

Parashas Va'eira

Learn the Lesson

"Chaim, make sure you do your homework before going outside to play."

"Okay, Mommy."

A short time later, Chaim goes outside to play.

"Chaim, that is wonderful! You did your homework so quickly!"

"Uh, not exactly, Mommy."

"Are you almost finished?"

"Well . . ."

"Chaim, don't tell me that you haven't done any homework yet."

"Umm . . ."

"Okay Chaim, I see that this problem is not going away so easily. I am afraid that I am going to have to punish you. First, I am warning you. The next time that you go out to play before doing your homework, you will not be allowed to go out the entire afternoon."

"Okay, Mommy."

Chaim thinks to himself, "Would Mommy really do that to me? I doubt it. I don't think that I have to worry about it."

The next day.
"Mommy, I'm going outside to play."
"Chaim, did you finish your homework?"
"Oh, I'm sorry, Mommy. I will do it when I come back. The boys are just starting a ball game now and I don't want to be late."
"Chaim, I am afraid that you won't be going to that ball game."
"But Mommy, I have to go to the ball game. The guys are all expecting me to be there."
"Chaim, do you remember what I told you yesterday about doing your homework before you go out to play?"
"Now I remember, Mommy. I'm sorry that I forgot. Will you let me go out to play now?"
"I'm sorry Chaim, but apologizing is not enough. I told you that you must do your homework before going out or you will be punished. Now I must keep my word. You cannot go outside the whole afternoon."
"Please, Mommy. Let me go out. I will do all of my homework first. I won't ever go out to play before doing homework."
"Chaim, let me tell you a story. I am sure that you will recognize it. There was once an evil king named Pharaoh. He treated the Jewish people very badly. He enslaved them, putting them to work with cruel, hard labor. He tortured them, killed them, and tried to demoralize them in every way.

Hashem sent Moshe Rabbeinu to take the Jewish people out of slavery. Moshe delivered a message from Hashem to Pharaoh, 'Let my nation go.' Pharaoh was warned, 'If you do not let the Jewish people go, you will be punished with plagues.' He did not listen. And so the plagues came. They were terrible."

"I know what the plagues were, Mommy. Blood, frogs, lice, wild animals . . ."

"Very good, Chaim. Let's take the plague of frogs. There were so many of them in Egypt, and they were croaking so loud that you could not hear yourself think. Pharaoh told Moshe to take away the frogs and he would let the Jewish people go. What do you think happened, Chaim?"

"Moshe got rid of the frogs and Pharaoh did not send out the Jewish people."

"Right. The same thing happened during the plague of wild animals. In the midst of the plague, Pharaoh was so terrorized by the animals that he promised to send the Jews out. As soon as the plague stopped . . ."

"He forgot all about it."

"Right, Chaim. The plague was a punishment sent to him by Hashem to teach him a lesson. While he was being punished, he said that he had learned his lesson. After the punishment was over, he went right back to his old ways. He did not learn his lesson. Therefore Hashem had to keep punishing him."

"I understand, Mommy."

"Believe me, Chaim, I do not like punishing you. However, you need to learn a lesson about homework. Now if you correct the problem and always do your homework before you go out to play, there will be no need for me to punish you again."

"Mommy, I must tell you something and I know that it sounds corny."

"Go ahead, Chaim."

"Thank you very much for loving me and caring about me enough to punish me. If you did not love me, you would just let me do whatever I want. I am going to learn the lesson from the punishment and always do my homework first."

"Chaim, you have taught me a lesson about how wonderful and appreciative a son can be."

"Mommy, I guess we have both learned a lesson."

Kinderlach . . .

There are two ways to learn a lesson. The easy way and the hard way. The easy way is to listen the first time. Then everyone is happy. The hard way is to receive a punishment. No one likes punishment. Parents do not like to give it and kinderlach surely do not like to receive it. So, let's all do things the easy way. Learn the lesson and skip the punishment.

The Voice of Peace

"Avi, you took my ball!"

"You gave me permission to play with it!"

"No I didn't!"

The two brothers begin to fight. Mommy, who was listening in the next room, calmly steps in.

"Come, boys. Let's not fight. There is nothing to be gained, and a lot to be lost. Making peace is the best thing."

The boys calm down and Avi smiles at his Mommy.
"Mommy, your soft words always make peace."

"This was Aharon and Moshe to whom Hashem said, 'Take the Children of Israel out of Egypt'" (*Shemos* 6:26). The Malbim comments that theirs was a twofold mission: the physical redemption from the slavery, and spiritual salvation from the impurity of Egyptian society. Moshe Rabbeinu had the main responsibility for the physical redemption. He spoke to Pharaoh. He initiated most of the plagues. Aharon, the Kohen, shouldered the burden of the spiritual salvation. He uplifted the spirits of a downtrodden people who did not know the ways of Hashem. Why were his words heard? Because he loved and pursued peace. His soft words warmed their hearts.

Kinderlach . . .

Who do you listen to? To someone who shouts at you and makes a fool of himself? Or to one who speaks softly and patiently... Aharon was able to make peace between people. Therefore his words were able to raise the Jewish people from the lowest levels of impurity. He is a role model for us. Speak kind words of encouragement and peace to everyone. Lift up yourself and those around you.

Parashas Bo

You Become What You Do

"Hi Mommy, I'm home."

"Avi! How are you? How was school?"

"Okay, I guess."

"What's wrong, Avi? You look a little sad."

"I don't know, Mommy."

"You just went to the doctor two days ago, so we know that you are healthy. You have been getting plenty of sleep and eating well."

"I know, Mommy. It's not my health."

"Is anyone bothering you in school? Are any of the neighbors pestering you?"

"No, Mommy. Everyone treats me great."

"Do you have a lot of schoolwork that is pressuring you?"

"No more than normal, Mommy."

"It sounds like nothing is really wrong. You are probably just going through a little down period, Avi."

"I think you are right, Mommy. How do I get out of it?"

"First of all, Avi, put a smile on your face."

"But I don't feel like smiling, Mommy."

"You should smile anyway, Avi."

"But Mommy, isn't there something wrong with that? Isn't it false to smile when you are not really happy?"

"Avi, you probably also think that it is wrong to give charity if you are not really generous. Or that it is wrong to study if you are not really studious. Or that it is wrong to help people if you are not really kind."

"Isn't it wrong to pretend, Mommy?"

"Sometimes it is, Avi. However, many times it is the best thing that you can do. One of our great Rabbis wrote a book about the 613 Mitzvos entitled the "Sefer HaChinuch." In this week's parasha we find mitzvah number sixteen, the prohibition against breaking any of the bones of the Pesach sacrifice. The Sefer HaChinuch sets down a basic principle there that is his key to personal growth and development: a person becomes what he does. If you want to change yourself in any way, begin with action."

"What do you mean, Mommy?"

"If you want to be happy, Avi, begin by acting happy."

"Will that really make me happy, Mommy?"

"Most certainly, Avi. Perhaps not right away, but after days, weeks, and months of acting happy, you will surely become as happy as you seem. If you want to become kind, then help people. Even if you do not feel like it. Help people whenever you have the opportunity. Again, after months and years of helping people, you will become a kind-hearted person. If you want to become generous, give gifts and charity."

"But Mommy, it sounds like you are just telling me to develop good habits."

"That is a big part of it, Avi. You should try to make good behavior into second nature. But the Sefer HaChinuch is saying much more than that. You will not become a sad person with a good habit of acting happy. You will actually become a truly happy person, inside and out."

"How can that be, Mommy? How can you change your insides like that?"

"That is the way Hashem created a person, Avi. I guess you can say that the heart is connected to the body. If you can get your body to do a mitzvah over and over and over again, you heart will come to love that mitzvah. Now come, Avi, let's try it. Exercise those face muscles and give me a nice big smile."

"I love you, Mommy."

"Avi, you are smiling from ear to ear. I'll bet you feel happier already."

"I don't just feel happier, Mommy, I am happier. You are so good to me, Mommy."

"That is because I love you, Avi. My heart is drawn after my deeds. I gave birth to you and have cared for you your whole life. How can I help but love you?"

"Mommy, I am going to follow your example. I am going to do mitzvos all of the time. Then I will become a real mitzvah boy."

"Avi, you are already doing one very big mitzvah."

"What is that, Mommy?"

"Making your mother very happy, and very, very proud of you."

> *Kinderlach . . .*
> *You become what you do. What do you want to be? Patient? Do it: speak softly at all times and act calm. You will become a patient person. Industrious? Do it: begin your day on time, don't be late for anything, and finish as quickly as you can. You will become a real go-getter. Satisfied? Do it: never complain about anything and express appreciation for everything. You will be so happy and satisfied with Hashem's gifts. You can become whatever you want. Just do it.*

Unforgettable

"Daddy, why are you slowing the car?"

"Something very important happened at that upcoming intersection, Avi. Ten years ago I was driving up this street and entered that intersection. A car came speeding through the red light and hit our car at full speed."

"Oh no! Who was in the car?"

"The entire family. A tremendous miracle happened — no one was hurt."

"Wow."

"I will never forget it. The vividness of the miracle is etched forever in my memory."

"In order to tell your children and grandchildren how I made a mockery of Egypt, and My signs that I placed upon them — that you may know that I am Hashem" (*Shemos* 10:2). The Ohr HaChaim HaKadosh has a deep insight into this verse. The ultimate purpose of the *makkos*, the Plagues of Egypt, was not to take revenge upon Pharaoh and his nation. Rather, the *makkos* were a sign to the Jewish people. We saw with our own eyes how Hashem ruled over all of the forces of nature. The wind, the water, the dust, the insects, the animals, and the fire were all at His command. Not just that, but He used them all to afflict and make a mockery of Pharaoh and his powerful nation, in a way that was never seen before by human eyes. This experience stayed etched in our memories for thousands of years.

Kinderlach . . .

People recall good events with fond memories. The day your baby brother took his first steps. The day of your bar mitzvah. The family reunion. We, the Jewish nation, do not have to search for good memories. Hashem has provided us with the best: the day we left Egypt. We remember it in our daily prayers, in the Kiddush on Shabbos and Yom Tov, and at the Seder night on Pesach. Think of these good memories whenever you can, kinderlach. Hashem is All Powerful, and He is ready to help you. Enjoy that warm feeling in your heart that comes from recalling fond memories.

Parashas Beshallach

Our Protector

"Look at that Egyptian, he sank straight to the bottom of the Sea of Reeds like a piece of lead. He drowned instantly."

"I recognize him. He was my taskmaster and he was fair to me. That other one is not having it so easy. He is going down slower, like a stone."

"He was not so good to the Jews, but there were worse ones than him. Look at that one over there."

"He is going up and down, over and over again, like a piece of straw. He is choking, gagging and struggling, but not drowning. He was very cruel to the slaves. Look at how Hashem is punishing him." (Based on *Rashi, Shemos* 15:5.)

"Hashem will make war for you, and you will remain silent" (*Shemos* 14:14). The Mechilta comments that Hashem's fighting was not limited to that one time. All throughout history, He will wage war against our enemies. The Meshech Chochma explains that Hashem was brought to fight for two reasons. First, the Jews did *t'shuva*, they repented. Second, they had a good argument: "Why did you take us out of Egypt to die here in the wilderness?" Even if we do not have such an argument, Hashem in His infinite kindness will continue to fight for us.

> *Kinderlach . . .*
> *Our enemies outnumber us, they are stronger, and they have more weapons. What can we do? How can we win? Only with the help of Hashem can we win. This story has repeated itself many times during the days of the Prophets and Judges. The people sinned and their enemies got the upper hand. The people did t'shuva and their enemies were defeated. Hashem fought for them. He will fight for us too. However, we must do t'shuva. Now is the time.*

Mitzvos Are Forever

"What did you get?"

"That Egyptian gave me all of his gold jewelry."

"I got a sack of silver coins."

"We're rich! After all of these years of slave labor in Egypt, we are finally getting what we deserve."

"Where is our leader Moshe? Why isn't he taking spoils?"

"Moshe took the bones of Yosef with him" (*Shemos* 13:19). The Tosefta (*Sota* 4:2) relates that the entire nation was busy gathering spoils from Egypt. Except for Moshe. He was busy with mitzvos. He was fulfilling Yosef's directive to take his bones up out of Egypt. As the verse states, "The wise of heart will take good deeds" (*Mishlei* 10:8). The Malbim explains this verse to mean that a person is constantly struggling with his *yetzer hara*, his evil inclination. He wants to do mitzvos, which are good for him, yet his *yetzer* tries to trick him into doing sins. A wise-hearted man overcomes this desire. A person only takes what he truly wants, and the wise-hearted man truly wants mitzvos. Therefore, he takes them.

The K'li Yakar offers a fascinating explanation of "Moshe took the bones of Yosef **with him**". What does a person take with him into the next world? Not his money. Nor his possessions. Only his mitzvos. That is the only thing that stays **with him** forever. Moshe took this mitzvah with him into eternity. Perhaps this is why Hashem presented Moshe with this particular mitzvah at this point in time: caring to the needs of the departed reminds us of that day when we will all be judged for our mitzvos. The Jewish people needed a reminder of what was truly valuable, at a time when they were busy with matters of this world, gathering spoils from Egypt.

Kinderlach . . .
What makes a person truly rich? Gold? Silver? Diamonds? Real-estate? Wrong on all counts. Mitzvos are the most valuable thing that a person can own. Who is a wise-hearted person? One who takes mitzvos. Where does he take them? Along with him into the next world. Mitzvos are forever.

Parashas Beshallach

Always in the Sea

"And the Children of Israel came through the sea on dry land" (*Shemos* 14:22). Contrast this with the verse, "And the Children of Israel went on dry land through the sea" (*Shemos* 14:29). Why did the two verses switch the words "dry land" and "sea"? The Noam Elimelech answers this question as follows.

When the Jewish people were going through the Sea of Reeds, they saw and felt the awesome miracles that Hashem had done for them. They were able to walk through the sea like a man who is walking on the ground. Contemplation of these wonders brought them to an even higher level. They realized that all of nature is as much of a miracle as the splitting of the sea. This is the level of "dry land through the sea". When you are on dry land, in your ordinary daily life, you see yourself as if you were in the Sea of Reeds. You see the miracles of nature just as you see the miracle of the splitting of the sea.

Our Sages mention three things that are as difficult for Hashem to do as splitting the sea: providing a person with his food and sustenance, finding him his spouse, and keeping his body functioning properly. Imagine all the might and power that it took to split the sea. The precision to blaze twelve tunnels through the water, tile them with marble floors, supply them with fruit trees and beautiful aromas. And the drowning of the Egyptians in the sea. This was a technological feat unparalleled in history! Or was it? Our Sages tell us that these other three feats are equally amazing. We just have to work a little harder to see the hidden miracles in these events.

> *Kinderlach . . .*
> *Just imagine that you were there at the Sea of Reeds. The situation looked hopeless. Then you plunged into the sea. The water was cold, up to your nose. Suddenly the sea split, in all of its glory and beauty. You were saved and the Egyptians were drowned. Imagine how you would sing to Hashem with all your heart. That is how you should say* Shiras HaYam *every day. Did you eat a delicious lunch today? Hashem's providing that food is as big a miracle as the splitting of the sea. Are you healthy? Another miracle. What about Mommy and Daddy? How did they find each other to be married? Yet another miracle. Think of all these miracles and put all your heart into thanking Hashem for your parents, and for all His kindness.*

Parashas Yisro

The Proper Setting

"Chaim, I have a question that has been bothering me for weeks now."

"Please tell it to me. Maybe I can answer it, Avi."

"Okay, Chaim. Here goes. Let's say that you were in charge of organizing a big event."

"How big, Avi?"

"The biggest. Hundreds of thousands of people involved. An awesome, spectacular, once-in-history event."

"Wow."

"That's right, Chaim, wow. Now here is my question. Where would you stage this event?"

"Let me think for a minute, Avi. Hmmm. How about the Swiss Alps? That is some of the most breathtaking scenery in the world."

"That's good, Chaim. Do you have any other suggestions?"

"What about the Grand Canyon? That is also an awesome 'wonder of the world.' Or, if you prefer a more urban setting, how about one of the world's great cities like New York, Tokyo, or London?"

"Good, good. Keep going."

"What about the lush tropical rainforest of Africa? The beauty there is unmatched anywhere in the world."

"Chaim, you're not going to believe this. I also thought of many of the same places as you."

"So what is your question, Avi?"

"Tell me Chaim, what was the most significant event in history?"

Chaim thinks for a minute, then answers.

"The giving of the Torah on Mt. Sinai. Hashem revealed Himself to the entire Jewish people—over two million men, women, and children."

"Exactly, Chaim. My question is this: if this was such an earth-shattering event, why did it take place in such a plain location? Mt. Sinai is in the desert. A barren wilderness. And if that isn't enough, Mt. Sinai is not even a very big mountain. It is quite low and ordinary. How is this an appropriate setting for such a monumental event?"

"Avi, your question is brilliant. Our great sages ask the very same question. To answer the question, close your eyes and try to imagine that you are among the two million people arriving at that piece of desert in front of the mountain. What is the first thing that strikes you?"

"That there is nothing here in the desert."

"Right. If you want to grow up to be a big Torah sage you have to make yourself like that desert. Nothing but Torah for you. Now, are your eyes still closed, Avi?"

"Yes."

"Good. What is the next thing that you notice?"

"That Mt. Sinai is a low mountain."

"Excellent! Why did Hashem choose a low mountain? To teach us that Torah can only come to humble people. We have to lower ourselves, like that mountain. We have to listen patiently to our teachers and study partners. We have to be ready to learn from everyone. As Ben Zoma teaches us in *Pirkei Avos* (4:1), 'Who is a wise man? A person who learns from all people.'"

"That's really amazing, Chaim."

"So you see, Avi, Mt. Sinai was the perfect place for the giving of the Torah. It taught the Jewish people what acquiring the Torah was all about."

"Let us not forget the last thing that happened there, Chaim."

"What was that, Avi?"

"That the entire Jewish people was united as never before, 'like one man with one heart.' Unity is a requirement for receiving the Torah."

"Avi, we should all strive to work on our humility, our Torah study, and our unity, so that we may all merit to receive the Torah in its entirety, just as they did on that day, 3200 years ago."

"Amen."

> *Kinderlach . . .*
> *Chaim and Avi have given us the keys to successful Torah learning. Cut out all distractions that will take your mind off your studies. Humble yourselves and patiently listen to the words of the teacher. Your study partner has much to teach you also. Strengthen your ties with friends, family, and neighbors. Torah and unity go hand in hand. We look forward to seeing you become great Torah scholars.*

Like Any Other Mitzvah

"Chaim, I must tell you something very important."

"Sure, Mommy. What is it?"

"I see that you have been playing in the street lately."

"Sure, Mommy. The boys like to play out there. We have more room to run."

"It is important to have room to run, Chaim, but I must tell you that the street is very dangerous. Buses, taxis, and cars speed down the streets."

"I know Mommy, but we are careful. We watch out for cars."

"Chaim, I know that you are careful. However, no matter how careful you are, an accident can still happen. There have been many traffic accidents in our neighborhood. I am sure that all of those children who were in accidents thought that it would never happen to them because they were careful."

"But Mommy, everybody plays in the street. All of my friends do it. Do you want me to give up my friends?"

"Of course not, Chaim. Maybe you can convince them not to play in the street."

"Mommy, I just cannot do it."

"Hmmm. I didn't expect you to say that. Let me ask you something, Chaim."

"Sure Mommy."

"Would you ever think of eating meat and milk together?"

"Of course not, Mommy. It's not kosher."

"Would you ever think of not sitting in the Sukkah on Succos? Or not eating matzah on Pesach?"

"Of course not, Mommy. They are mitzvos written in the Torah."

"Chaim, listening to your parents is also a mitzvah written in the Torah. It is in this week's parasha. 'Honor your father and mother' (*Shemos* 20:12). If you would not think about violating the laws of kashrus or Pesach or Sukkos, because they are written in the Torah, then you must also listen to your parents because it is written in the Torah."

"I never thought about it that way, Mommy."

"Chaim, you are such a good boy, and I know that you want to do every mitzvah that you can. Why do you sometimes not listen to Daddy and me?"

"Because I didn't see it as a mitzvah."

"Exactly."

Kinderlach . . .
Sometimes we do not feel like listening to Daddy and Mommy. It's too hard. We're tired. We're busy. Nobody's doing it. We feel that we can say no if we want. We think that listening to them is like listening to our friend. It is not. The next time that you feel like contradicting your parents, stop a second and think: "This is a mitzvah written in the Torah. I have to take it as seriously as I do other mitzvos. No fooling around here." "Here I come, Mommy. Right away. I have a mitzvah to do!"

Parashas Mishpatim

Damage Control

"Chaim, what is that on your leg?"
"It's a cast, Avi."
"*Oy vey*. What happened?"
"I broke my leg."
"*Oy vey, vey, vey*. You should have a '*refuah sh'laimah!*' (speedy recovery)."
"Thank you so much, Avi."
"If you don't mind my asking, Chaim, how did it happen?"

"I was walking home from school, and I slipped on a skateboard that someone had left on the sidewalk. I fell down right onto my left leg and broke it."

"I'll bet that hurt."

"It sure did. But you know there is a positive side to everything."

"Really, Chaim? If you can find a positive side to falling down and breaking your leg, then you deserve a big reward."

"I can really appreciate the Torah's laws of damages."

"Where does the Torah mention damages, and what type of damage does the Torah talk about?"

"Believe it or not, Avi, it is in this week's parasha, Mishpatim, the Torah mentions property damage and personal injury. In my case, someone was careless and left their skateboard in a public area. They are responsible for the damage that the skateboard causes."

"Does the Torah mention bicycle riding?"

"Not exactly, but the Gemara (*Bava Kamma*) writes about speeding through a public place. A person is responsible to drive or walk safely."

"Really, Chaim. This is so interesting. Please tell me more."

"If we have pets or other animals, we must make sure that they do not hurt other people or damage their property. If we light a fire, we must make sure that it does not burn out of control. When we borrow something from someone, we must be sure to return it to him in the same condition that we received it. We must pay if it is lost or stolen."

"Chaim, I thought these things were all common sense."

"They are, Avi, but they are from the Torah. Most of the important ideas and laws in the world have their origins in the Torah. The Torah is Hashem's wisdom. He has a lot more common sense than we do."

"After what happened to you, I am sure that you will never leave anything dangerous lying on the sidewalk."

"That is for sure, Avi. As I said, there is a positive side to everything. After reading about these laws in this week's parasha, I realize how careful a person must be not to hurt others. Having things is a privilege, but also a responsibility. We must make sure that our possessions do not damage someone. We also have to be very careful that we ourselves do not hurt someone. Safety and consideration are very important Torah laws."

"I guess you can say that the Torah is concerned about 'damage control,' Chaim."

"You're not kidding, Avi. Don't wait until an accident happens. Start your 'damage control' now, before it is too late."

Kinderlach . . .
Be careful. Do not leave your things lying around where they can hurt people. Be gentle with things that can easily break. Go slowly in crowded places. Be careful when you turn the corner or when you cannot see ahead of you. Treat other people's things as if they were your own. Don't even think about vandalism. Respecting other people's property is the alef-beis of good behavior.

Compromise

"Tzippy, can you please wash off the porch?"

"I already did, Daddy."

"It still looks dirty to me."

"It must have been the dirty water dripping down from the neighbor's porch."

Tzippy's Daddy is upset. He goes storming up to the neighbor, knocking on the door.

"Did you just wash your porch?"

"Yes."

"The water spilled down on to my nice clean porch."

"This is the tenth time that you have complained about this and I have told you every time that it is not my problem."

"If you do not stop this I am going to *Beis Din* (Rabbinical Court)."

"Suit yourself."

Tzippy's Daddy comes downstairs even more upset. He knows that going to Beis Din *is not easy. But what choice does he have?*

"How did it go with the neighbor, Daddy?"

"Not good. I may have to go to *Beis Din* to settle this."

"Really? We were just learning about *Beis Din* today in our parasha class."

"What did you learn, Tzippy?"

"The teacher taught us what the Baal HaTurim wrote about the word *mishpatim* in the very first verse. The letters of the word form an acronym in Hebrew. 'The judge is commanded to make a compromise between the two parties before he judges.' When you go to *Beis Din,* Daddy, the first thing that the *Dayan* (Rabbinical Judge) will do is try to reach a compromise between you and our neighbor."

"If that is the case, then why don't I try to reach a compromise with him now? It will save us a lot of time, expense, aggravation, and ill feelings."

"Great idea, Daddy."

Tzippy's Daddy goes upstairs with a good attitude.

"I have an idea. Why don't we make a schedule so that you wash your porch before we wash ours? Then your dirty water will not fall onto our clean porch."

"No problem. I'm always ready to compromise."

Kinderlach . . .

Compromise is a wonderful thing. Each side gives in a little and they come to a settlement. "Estie, it is time to go to sleep." "I want to stay up another half hour, Mommy." "That is too late." "How about another twenty minutes?" "Estie, make it ten minutes and we have a deal." "Okay, Mommy. Ten minutes." Kinderlach, now is the time to master the skill of compromising. It may take some practice, but it is definitely worthwhile. You will avoid most of life's petty arguments. Your life will be much more peaceful, happy, and relaxed.

Parashas Terumah

Beautiful Music

The experiment was about to begin. The special soundproofed room was absolutely silent. In the middle sat two musical instruments—a small violin and a huge bass fiddle, both perfectly tuned. The violinist expertly drew his bow across the violin string, bringing out a perfect "C" note. Everyone waited with baited breath. Yes, they could hear it. The string of the bass fiddle was vibrating, also playing a perfect "C". The instruments were in perfect harmony, and the bass played without even being touched.

The Malbim uses this parable to describe the relationship between man and the world. Hashem designed the universe with a master plan. All of the forces and the events that He executes in all of the worlds are all directed by the actions of . . . man. We are compared to the little violin, and the universe to the big bass. If we listen to and play the sweet tunes of Hashem's mitzvos, then the universe will reverberate with beautiful music. Wonderful events, filled with blessing, are the result. However, if we play the sad, lamenting music that comes from sins, the big universe will respond with destruction and suffering.

> *Kinderlach . . .*
> *Many people are putting much thought into shaping world events. There are so many crises, and so many situations that seem helpless. We just keep hearing more and more sad music. We can change all of that. If we begin playing happy tunes, the world will respond. The next time you pray, sing a beautiful song to Hashem. Tell Him how much you love Him and His mitzvos. Give charity with a big smile on your face, thanking the poor person for giving you the opportunity to fulfill this mitzvah. Let the melody of Torah learning fill your heart. Waltz through the day, twirling around mitzvah after mitzvah. Make beautiful music and change the world.*

Give and Take

"Welcome, welcome. We hope you enjoy your stay here. How was your trip?"

"A bit rough, especially at the end."

"Baruch Hashem, it is over."

"May I trouble you for a hot drink?"

"I would very much like to help you, however, we do not serve hot drinks here."

"Really? Well, I'll just go and get one myself. One minute, where is my wallet? Did you see my wallet? It seems to be missing."

"No, I did not see it."

"It's not important. I can use my credit card. Oy vey, I seem to have lost my credit cards also. This was really a rough trip."

"I wish I could help you."

"Can you order a hot drink for me from the nearest restaurant, and I will reimburse you?"

"I'm afraid that I can't do that."

The man begins to get upset.

"What is going on here? All I want is a simple hot drink. Now why can't you give it to me?"

"Ummm."

"Do you realize who I am? I am a multi-millionaire. I own real estate in every major city in the world. I have a fleet of cars and a private plane. If you don't give me a hot drink, I am going to phone my attorney and sue you. I can buy and sell this place ten times over."

The man behind the counter looks through his records.

"Here is your file. I see your account balance."

"Good. Now you can see how wealthy I am. Now please, order a hot drink for me."

"Your account is a modest sum, but it certainly is not millions."

"What?!? Let me see that record. There must be some mistake. What is going on here?"

The man looks the newcomer in the eye and began to explain.

"Sir, you have arrived here because your life on earth has ended. You fulfilled your mission down there and therefore you were summoned here. You do not bring your earthly possessions with you here. All of your cars, planes and millions are gone."

The man thinks for a long time, letting the impact of the words sink in.
"I see. This is it. Olam Habba, the Next World."
"Yes."
"But you said that I have a bank balance here. I thought that I could not bring any money with me."
"With one exception. Your bank balance is the money that you gave to *tsedaka*, charity, when you were alive. That is the only money that you bring with you."

The man thought about all of his millions, and how he spent them on so many different things. He recalled how he was not so courteous to those who came to collect charity.
"Oy vey. I should have given more. Now it is too late."

"Take for Me *trumah*" (Shemos 25:2). The verse uses the word "take" instead of "give" when referring to *trumah* (charitable gifts). Why? Because this is the only money that you can "take" with you . . . into eternity.

Kinderlach . . .
Tsedaka is big business. You can make tremendous profits. The more you give, the more you take. Money comes and goes, but tsedaka stays with you forever. Give, give, give, and take, take, take.

Parashas Tetzaveh

Guiding Light

"Avi, it sure is dark in here."

"Where are the rest of the guys on the tour, Chaim?"

"I think they went the other way. They continued through the main cave, but we wanted to see this side tunnel."

"I'm nervous, Avi."

"Don't worry. Chaim. I'm right behind you."

"That's what I'm worried about, Avi. No one is in front of me and I can't see anything."

"Just go slowly and feel your way along. Are there any rocks or holes on the floor of this cave?"

"I can't see any."

Suddenly the boys are frightened by a loud noise.
Boom!

"What was that, Chaim?"

"I fell down. I must have tripped over something. Oww. My foot hurts. How did we get ourselves into this predicament anyway?"

"We decided to leave the tour and explore this little tunnel. Before we knew it, there was no light."

"I think I found a light. Yes, here is a flashlight. Wow! Let's turn it on."

"Wow. One little light illuminates this whole dark place. Look at that, Chaim. You tripped over a rock."

"I see, Avi. Baruch Hashem we have this light, or I could have fallen into that pit over there."

"Baruch Hashem."

"Come, let us find our way back to the rest of the class."

And so the boys slowly find their way out of the tunnel to join up with their classmates.

"Look! There are Chaim and Avi! We were so worried about you guys. Where were you? What is that in your hand, Chaim?"

"It is an old flashlight that I found. It saved our lives."

"How?"

"We had wandered into a dark cave and were totally lost. There was no light. We could have fallen into a deep pit. Then, I found this light and turned it on. It guided us back to the tour with you guys."

"The light guided you. That is exactly what our teacher, Rabbi Levy, was teaching us about this week's parasha."

"Which light are you referring to?"

"The Menorah, the light in the *Mishkan* (Tabernacle). The verse says, 'And they shall take pure, pressed olive oil for the light, to kindle the lamp continually' (*Shemos* 27:20). The Midrash compares this oil and the light that it sheds to the light of Torah. A person without Torah is compared to someone who is walking in the dark. He trips and falls over all sorts of obstacles. The obstacles are sins, and he falls into their trap.

However, one who toils in Torah is like a person walking with a lamp in his hand. He will not stumble because the light guides his way. Similarly, the light of Torah steers us clear of sin, and guides us on our journey through life."

"That is exactly what happened to us. Without that light, we surely would have fallen and gotten seriously hurt."

Kinderlach . . .

Without the light of Torah, we are sure to trip and fall over many obstacles in life. We have many challenges, tests, and opportunities in our lives. The Torah always steers us in the right direction. Hashem's Torah is the light that guides us how to live our lives. Without it we will surely get lost. With it, we will accomplish tremendous things. Chaim and Avi thought they would find adventure in a dark cave. Instead, they found danger. They thought they found a flashlight. But really, they found the Torah. Our guiding light.

Holy Garments

"You shall make holy garments for Aharon your brother, for glory and splendor" (*Shemos* 28:2). Thus the Torah begins the description of the special garments worn by the *Kohanim* (Priests) during their service in the Temple. The *K'sav Sofer* in his commentary on the Torah discusses these garments as well as other types of Jewish clothing. He writes that rabbinical garments worn by Torah sages give glory to them and the Torah they represent. They also serve as a constant reminder to them of the elevated stature of a Torah sage. One of the distinguishing features of the Jews in Egypt was their clothing. They did not fall to the lowest level of impurity. Instead they retained their special clothing, names, and language. This is what protected them. We see how important it is for a Jew to dress properly.

The Pele Yo'etz sets down guidelines for proper dress. The middle path is the best. Clothing should not be too fancy or expensive, because this can bring pride and arrogance to a person. Additionally, extravagant clothing sets a fashion trend and puts pressure upon those who cannot afford such expensive clothes. At the other extreme, clothing should not be ragged, torn, or dirty. Such clothing does not honor the person wearing it. The Jewish people, Hashem's chosen nation, dress in a dignified manner that gives honor to their Creator and His Torah. We are not subject to the whims and styles of the fashions of the day. Our clothes remind us who we are, and what we are doing in this world.

Kinderlach . . .

Don't you feel good when you get dressed up in your best clothes for Shabbos? You almost feel like a different person. You see what a big effect clothes can have on a person. Perhaps you can ask Daddy or Mommy to review with you the laws of modesty in dress. Develop good dressing habits now, and they will stay with you the rest of your lives.

Parashas Ki Sisa

The Sign

"What a beautiful day to walk home from school together, Avi."

"It sure is, Chaim. The air is so fresh and clean."

"Do you mind if we stop at the grocery store for a minute? My Mom asked me to pick up something for her."

"Why not? There is Frankel's Deli across the street."

"Look at that, Avi. The door is locked and the deli is all dark inside. It looks as if he's closed up."

"I hope everything is okay. Mr. Frankel is a really nice man."

A few days later, the boys walk by the deli again.

"Hi boys! How are you doing?"

"Great, Mr. Frankel. How are you?"

"Just fine, boys."

"That's good. We were a little worried when we came by a few days ago. The store was closed."

"Thanks for your concern, boys. I was in the hospital for a few days. Nothing serious, *Baruch Hashem*. Now I am feeling better and the business is going as strong as ever."

"We're happy that both you and your store are doing well."

"Do you see that sign above the door of my store?"

"Sure, Mr. Frankel. It says, 'Frankel's Deli.'"

"Right, boys. Just remember this. As long as that sign is up, the store is still in business. If, Heaven forbid, that sign comes down, then you know that I had to close down the business."

"Mr. Frankel, that is just what the Chafetz Chaim said!"

"What? He never came into my store. He never even saw this place. He passed away long before I was even born."

"Mr. Frankel, you have a good sense of humor. We are talking about a parable that the Chafetz Chaim told about a store. It is based on a verse in this week's parasha. 'Between Me and the Children of Israel it (the Shabbos) is an eternal sign' (*Shemos* 31:17). Shabbos is a sign between Hashem and each and every Jew. It is that Jew's identification that his soul is part of the Jewish nation. As long as he keeps the Shabbos, he identifies himself as a part of the Nation of Israel. Just like your store, Mr. Frankel. That sign is your identification. As long as the sign is up, we know that you are still in business. Even if the store is closed for a little while. If you take down the sign, then we know that the business has closed down. Similarly with Shabbos observance. If a Jew, Heaven forbid, no longer observes the Shabbos, then he has taken down his sign."

"Boys, that's a great parable. I would love to spend more time talking with you, but today is Erev Shabbos, and it is getting late. I still have many preparations to do before I welcome the Shabbos Queen."

"So do we, Mr. Frankel. You should have lots of success in your business, and have a wonderful Shabbos!"

"You too, boys. Good Shabbos!"

> Kinderlach . . .
> Shabbos is such an important mitzvah. It is the sign that binds us to Hashem. What can we do to strengthen our observance of the Shabbos? Perhaps we can take time to increase our knowledge of the laws of Shabbos. When you learn something new, put it into practice. Let us all try to be ready for Shabbos a little earlier next week. Keep the neon lights on our sign glowing brightly.

Mercy

Moshe pleaded. But Hashem was adamant. The people had committed a grievous sin. Hashem would not go up with them into the Land of Milk and Honey. He would send an angel instead. If He accompanied them and they sinned again, He would have to annihilate them.

"Hashem, Hashem, God, Compassionate, and Gracious..." (*Shemos* 34:6). Hashem instructed Moshe to say these words of prayer. The Gemara (*Rosh Hashanah* 17b) states, "Whenever the Nation of Israel sins, let them pray this prayer and I shall forgive them." What is so special about this prayer? The words describe Hashem's Thirteen Attributes of Mercy. He is Compassionate and Merciful in every way possible. We appeal to His Mercy, and He in turn is merciful upon us. That seems simple. However, it is not the whole story. Rav Leib Chasman notes that the prayer alone will not help unless we do *t'shuva* (repentance). We must correct our mistakes.

We are asking Hashem to have mercy upon us. We can arouse His compassion by being merciful to others. This is the area of *t'shuva* that brings Heavenly Mercy. As the Gemara (*Shabbos* 151b) states, "All who have mercy upon Hashem's creatures, receive Mercy from Heaven." The Yalkut Shimoni on Parashas Eikev instructs us to act with kindness toward everyone.

> *Kinderlach . . .*
> *Every person that you see is an opportunity for doing* chessed, kindness. *Do you see someone in a hurry? Move aside to let him pass. Is your sister sad? Smile at her to cheer her up. Is Mommy overwhelmed with housework? Wash a few dishes. Is someone speaking to you? Pay close attention to him. Does your study partner have difficulty understanding the material? Explain it again. And again. Say thank you to Mommy for preparing lunch for you. These acts of kindness are like diamonds. They seem small, but they are so precious. They can arouse Hashem's Mercy and help the Jewish people.*

Parashas Vayakhel

Don't Wait Till The End

"Hi, Chaim. How many raffle tickets have you sold?"

"Eight."

"Wow, you are doing better than I am. I only sold five."

"We still have two weeks to go until the raffle drawing, Avi. We have to sell our book of ten by then. Here comes Mr. Weiss. Let's see if he is interested. Hi, Mr. Weiss!"

"Hi boys. How are you doing?"

"Great, Mr. Weiss. Did you know that our school is running a raffle to raise money to buy more books for the library?"

"I didn't know that."

"Would you be interested in buying a ticket? We hope to raise enough money to buy several sets of books, many biographies of Torah Giants, and a lot of children's storybooks."

"Boys, this is a great cause. I will do more than buy one ticket. Right before the raffle drawing, bring me all of your unsold ticket books and I will buy them all."

The boys' eyes widened.
"Really, Mr. Weiss?"

"Really. I will see you in a couple of weeks, boys. Remember, any raffles that you do not sell, I will buy."

The boys are so excited that they cannot wait to get to school to tell the librarian.

"Rabbi Sofer, we have great news!"

"Yes, boys."

"We found someone who will buy all of the unsold raffle tickets!"

"Boys, that's wonderful! However, we still must try to sell as many as we can. After all, we must be fair and not take advantage of this very generous person. Keep up the great work, boys. We'll have that set of Mishnayos and Rambam for our library quicker than you can say, 'Shalom Aleichem Rebbe.'"

Over the next two weeks, Avi and Chaim manage to sell many tickets. The big day finally arrives. Sure enough, every one of the raffle tickets is sold. The boys see Mr. Weiss on his way to the raffle drawing.

"Hi, boys! What's doing? How many tickets am I going to buy today? I want to make a nice donation to really help the school library."

"Ummm. Well. Uh."

"What's the matter, boys? Are you afraid that there are too many unsold tickets left? Don't worry. I told you that I would buy all of them. Now, how many are there."

"Ummm. Well."

"Come, boys. Let's not waste time. The drawing will be very soon. Now, here is my checkbook. How much should I write on the check?"

"Mr. Weiss, you are not going to believe this."

"Believe what?"

"All of the tickets were sold."

"Really?"

"Yes, really."

"Boys, I must say that I am disappointed. However, I should have known this was going to happen."

"How could you possibly have known?"

"I'll tell you boys, the same thing happened three thousand two hundred years ago, to our ancestors in the desert. And it is even in this week's parasha."

"Did they really have a raffle for the school library in the desert, Mr. Weiss?"

"No, boys, of course not. However, they had a tremendous fund-raising drive for the materials to build the *Mishkan* (Tabernacle). All of the Jewish people contributed. The princes of the twelve tribes wanted to give an extra special gift. They waited for the end, just as I did, in order to donate whatever was lacking. Guess what?"

"Nothing was missing."

"Exactly. The Jewish people were so generous that they had to be told to stop giving. There was nothing left for the princes to contribute. I should have known better. We were then, and are now, a nation of people who open their hearts generously to give. The princes learned their lesson and so will I. At the inauguration of the *Mishkan,* they were the first ones to bring their offerings. The next time you have a fundraising drive, boys, come to me first. I want to be the first one to give, not the last."

"Mr. Weiss, we have all learned a lesson about doing things quickly. If you wait till the end, you end up in last place."

> *Kinderlach . . .*
> *Let us try to have a contest to see who can be the first one to wash hands after Kiddush this Shabbos. Who will be the first one to be ready for school in the morning? Who will be the first one to change into pajamas in the evening? Hashem wrote the story of the princes into the Torah to teach us about quickness. It surely is important for us to try to do all of our mitzvos as promptly as possible.*

Make a Name for Yourself

"See, Hashem has proclaimed the name of Betzalel ben Uri ben Chur, of the tribe of Yehuda" (*Shemos* 35:30). The Midrash elaborates the many virtues of a good name. "A good name is better than good oil" (*Koheles* 7:1). The fragrance of good oil can only fill one room. However, a good name goes from one end of the world to the other. Rashi adds that oil flows downward from the head to the beard, but a good name keeps going higher and higher. Good oil lasts a short time, but a good name is forever.

"The day of death [is better] than the day of birth" (*ibid*). Why? On the day of birth, we do not know what a person will become. When he dies, his deeds become known. The Ibn Ezra explains that this is why the verse connects a good name to the day of death: to teach that a person's deeds determine his name. Good deeds will earn a good name. We proclaim Hashem's good Name in our daily prayers, "You are Holy and Your Name is Holy." For through Your deeds, we recognize Your Holiness.

Listen to how the Torah describes the birth of Moshe Rabbeinu. "A man from the house of Levi married a daughter of Levi. She became pregnant and gave birth to a son" (*Shemos* 2:1–2). No names are mentioned. Later, after Moshe achieved greatness, the Torah recounts his birth. "And Amram married his aunt Yocheved and she bore Aharon and Moshe" (*Shemos* 6:20). Now they had earned names for themselves.

Kinderlach . . .
How many good deeds did you do today? Ten? Twenty? A hundred? These good deeds earn you something very special. A good name. Avraham Avinu, Yitzchak Avinu, Yaakov Avinu, Yosef HaTzaddik, Moshe Rabbeinu, Aharon HaKohen, David HaMelech, Shlomo HaMelech, Rebbe Akiva, Rebbe Yehuda HaNassi, Rebbe Yochanan, and others were all tzaddikim. They earned great names for themselves with their outstanding deeds. Kinderlach, put your name on the list. Make a name for yourself.

Parashas Pikudei

Who's Counting?

"Do you have everything that you will need?"

"I'm not sure. Let's go through the checklist again."

Slowly they went down the list together, checking off every item.

"Everything is in order. You are now ready to leave on your mission. Remember, when you are finished you will have to return back here and give an accounting of everything that you were given to use on your mission."

"I understand."

"You should have much success. May Hashem be with you."

He made his way down the narrow tunnel until he was out of sight. When he reached the other end of the tunnel, two hands gently pulled him out.

"Mazel tov! Mazel tov! Your wife has just given birth to a baby boy."

"These are the accounts of the *Mishkan* (Tabernacle)" (*Shemos* 38:21). The Torah proceeds to give an exact accounting of all the gold, silver, and copper that was used in the building of the *Mishkan*. Why was this accounting necessary? Rav Moshe Feinstein answers that the Torah is teaching us a very important lesson. A person must give an accounting of everything that Hashem has given to him. What did he do with the precious time that Hashem gave him on this earth? Did he learn Torah and do mitzvos? Or did he waste his time on frivolities... What did he do with the livelihood that Hashem gave him? Did he give to charity? Or did he keep everything for himself... Was he blessed with good health? Intelligence? Skills? What did he do with all of these gifts? A person should not think that he can do whatever he pleases with what he was given. He will have to give an accounting for everything.

Kinderlach . . .

We are on a mission called life. Hashem gave us many things to use on this mission. He has a checklist of everything. He wants the best for us, therefore, He gave us the Torah which instructs us how to use everything. When we follow its instructions we will be the best that we can be. Did you learn well today? Or did you waste your time spent in school... Did you thank Mommy for preparing a delicious meal for you? Or did you let the opportunity to express your gratitude slip by... Did you give charity to the poor man who was collecting? Did you eat good healthy food that will make you stronger and healthier? Or did you waste your appetite on junk food... Hashem is keeping track of everything you do. He wants you to give a good accounting. Don't disappoint Him.

The Wise Heart

The Torah uses the expression *chacham leiv* many times in this week's parasha. Literally translated, *chacham leiv* means wise heart. Rav Leib Chasman asks the following question: when we speak about wisdom, we usually refer to the head, not the heart. Why does the Torah refer to the heart as being wise and not the head? He answers that a *chacham* (wise man) is not just someone who is able to speak and repeat words of wisdom. A *chacham* is someone who internalizes these words of wisdom, making them part of his heart. He lives by them. That is why he is referred to as *chacham leiv*. As it says in the third paragraph of the Shema, "Do not search after your **heart** and your eyes." Rashi explains that the heart controls the desires and motivations of a person. If we put wisdom into our hearts, then our whole lives will be governed by wisdom.

Kinderlach . . .
How do we put wisdom into our hearts? When we learn a bit of wisdom from the Torah, we take it to heart and do what it says. When we learn a new halacha, a new law, we put it into practice. What if you had just learned the laws of returning lost objects — and on your way home from school you see a lost object? Wonderful! Hashem has given you the opportunity to apply what you just learned! Let us say that you had learned the laws of washing hands before eating bread. The next time you wash, you will do it much more carefully and correctly, because you have learned all about it. When you implement what you learn, kinderlach, you will become truly wise of heart.

Trustworthiness

In the beginning of the Parasha, Moshe Rabbeinu gives a precise accounting of all of the gold, silver, and brass that were donated to the construction of the *Mishkan*, the Tabernacle. He lists how much of each was collected, and exactly what they were used for.

Rabbeinu Bechaye describes Moshe Rabbeinu as a man of trust. "He is the trusted one in all My house" (*Bamidbar* 12:7). Hashem trusted Moshe to be the keeper of all the treasures of the *Mishkan*. If Hashem trusted Moshe, then surely he was not suspected of stealing anything. Why then did Moshe Rabbeinu have to give an accounting to the people?

Rabbeinu Bechaye writes, "Just as a person has to fulfill his obligations to Hashem, so too he must fulfill his obligations to his fellow man." Even though he is honest, and Hashem knows that he is honest, he must still make sure that people know of his honesty. This is what it means when it says, "And you shall be clean (of suspicion) from Hashem and from Yisrael" (*Bamidbar* 32:22). A person has to place himself above suspicion.

Kinderlach . . .

Do you see how careful even a trustworthy person must be, in order not to appear suspicious? How does this apply to us? When we go out to play we should be considerate and tell Mommy where we are going, and who we are going to play with. Perhaps she will worry about us. When we come home from school we should tell our parents about our homework assignments and tests. We can also tell them that we have finished our homework. Then they will know that we are keeping up with our studies. We all know how much Daddy and Mommy love and care about us. We can show our appreciation by being sensitive to their concerns about us.

Simcha's Kinder Torah

Sefer Vayikra

Parashas Vayikra

Come Closer

"Boys, the principal is coming in five minutes to speak to the class. Everyone prepare themselves."

The boys rush to straighten up the class and then sit orderly in their seats. The principal arrives and everyone stands up.

"Boys, thank you for giving me a few minutes of your time. I know that you are very busy learning, so I will be brief. The director of the old-age home across the street asked me if some of our students could come to the home to visit with the people there. It would make the elderly people very happy and be a tremendous mitzvah. Therefore, I am asking each boy to sacrifice half an hour of his free time each week to visit with the people in the old-age home. Thank you very much. That's all, boys."

With that, everyone stands up as the principal leaves.
"Half an hour a week is a big sacrifice, Chaim."
"I don't think so, Avi. I don't consider it a sacrifice at all."
"But you have to give up half an hour."

"I'll tell you what I think about that, based on this week's parasha, Vayikra. The parasha begins with the sacrifices that were offered up on the Altar in the *Mishkan* (Tabernacle). However, the word sacrifice is misleading. Sacrifice means that you give up something. Even if you receive something in return, it is not as much as you gave. After all, you made a sacrifice. But the Hebrew word is *korban*. The root of that word is *karov,* meaning 'to come close.' A *korban* brings a person close."

"Close to what?"

"Close to Hashem. By giving of himself, he comes closer to Hashem."

"How can that be?"

"Rabbi Eliyahu Dessler, one of the great Torah leaders of the past generation, explains that you become close to someone by giving to him. The biggest proof is parents and children. No one loves children more than their parents do. Why? Because the parents give to them constantly. That creates a bond of love so strong that nothing can break it."

"I understand, Chaim. If we go to the old-age home, we do not sacrifice anything. By giving time and attention to the elderly people there, we will actually gain by becoming close to them."

"That's it, Avi. You don't lose by giving; you only gain. A close relationship with someone is one of the most precious things in the whole world. It is well worth the half an hour per week."

"Come, Chaim. Let's go to the old-age home right now. Those elderly people need our help. Thank you so much for bringing me close to this mitzvah of getting close to people."

> *Kinderlach . . .*
> *Look at those two boys. They are best friends. They would do anything for each other. How did they get so close? By giving to each other. Look at that mother and daughter. The mother would fly halfway across the world to help her daughter. Why does she love her so much? Because she gave to her from the minute she was alive. Get close to people. Give and give and give to them.*

Don't Embarrass

"Yaakov, the Pesach holiday is coming in a few weeks."

"I know, Rachel. I am preparing the sacrifice that we are bringing to the Beis HaMikdash."

"Are we bringing a big animal this year?"

Yaakov's eyes fell. He spoke hesitatingly, in a low voice.

"I am afraid that we cannot afford an animal this year. We will bring a grain offering instead."

"When a *nefesh* (person) offers a grain offering to Hashem . . . He shall bring it to the sons of Aaron, the Kohanim . . ." (*Vayikra* 2:1–2). The Baal HaTurim elaborates on the word *nefesh*, which also means soul. A poor person, who could not afford to bring an expensive animal, brought a grain offering instead. Even so, he put his soul into paying for that grain offering. Regular animals were sacrificed in public, where everyone would see. The grain offering, however, was brought privately, only to the Kohanim. The public would not see that he was too poor to bring an animal sacrifice. This would save him the embarrassment of not being able to offer as large a gift to Hashem as other people could.

> *Kinderlach . . .*
> *Do you see how the Torah is sensitive to people's feelings? This is a model for our behavior. Did your sister get a good grade on her test? Or was it not so good... Let her tell Mommy privately. Don't embarrass her in front of the family. Always knock before you open a closed door. Someone may be doing something private in the room. Don't ever make fun of someone's clothing or haircut. These things can be very embarrassing. Sensitivity to other's feelings is the true mark of good behavior.*

Humility

Rabbeinu Bechaye begins his commentary on the book of Vayikra by speaking about the humility of Moshe Rabbeinu. Moshe certainly had many attributes to be proud of. He was the head of all prophets. Of all his exemplary *middos* (character traits), the one that the Torah chose to praise was his humility. "The man, Moshe, was very humble"

(*Bamidbar* 12:3). Due to his humility he did not want to approach the *Mishkan* while the Divine Presence was resting there. Moshe Rabbeinu would not enter unless he was summoned. That is how *Sefer Vayikra* begins: "And Hashem called to Moshe." Moshe only came when he was called.

Kinderlach . . .

Humility is one of the finest attributes that we can acquire. Shlomo HaMelech relates (Mishle 22:4) that when one attains humility, then fear of Hashem, wealth, honor, and life also come to him.

How does one become humble? He should not rush to speak. He should have patience, honor others, and praise them. He is quiet when unflattering things are said about him. Sometimes, kinderlach, Daddy and Mommy have to correct our mistakes. It is not always pleasant to hear criticism. A humble person is quiet when being criticized. He listens and takes what is being said to heart. Kinderlach, the opposite of humility is the terrible middah of chutzpah. One who has chutzpah will never grow in his middos because he is not able to listen to any constructive criticism. We want to avoid chutzpah at all costs. B'ezras Hashem, kinderlach, we will all acquire Moshe Rabbeinu's middah of humility.

Parashas Tzav

The Vessel

"Knock knock, I'm home."

"Chaim, how are you? How was your day at school?"

"Great, Mommy. I'm so thirsty. May I please have a drink of water?"

"Sure, Chaim. Here is the pitcher, and here is a cup. Don't forget to make a *bracha* (blessing over the water) before you drink."

"Yum. That was so refreshing. Thank you so much Mommy. I was so thirsty that I would have used my hands as a cup, or even taken a drink from the pitcher.

"Your hands, Chaim, cannot hold nearly as much water as the cup. The water that you held would probably drip or spill as you were trying to drink. The best vessel to hold drinking water is a cup."

"What is the best vessel for holding paint, Mommy?"

"A sealed can. That way the paint will not dry out."

"What about toothpaste?"

"A tube is the best for that. You can squeeze out just as much as you need."

"And a bucket is the best thing to hold my building blocks."

"Right, Chaim. You could put them in a plastic bag, but the

bucket is much stronger."

"In other words, Mommy, there are different containers that we can use to hold things, but each thing has the vessel that suits it best."

"Exactly. Chaim, did you know that spiritual things have vessels also?"

"They must be spiritual vessels."

"They are, Chaim. We learn about a very important vessel from this week's parasha."

"Hmmm. Let's see. Parashas Tzav is all about *korbanos,* the offerings brought in the Tabernacle and Holy Temple. Do you mean the vessels used in preparing and sacrificing the *korbonos,* Mommy?"

"Not exactly, Chaim. There was a *korban* called the *shlamim,* the peace offering."

"Why was it called that, Mommy?"

"The Midrash Rabba explains that it was called *shlamim* because it made peace between the *Kohanim* (Priests), the *Mizbeach* (Altar), and the man who brought the *korban.*"

"How did it make peace, Mommy?"

"Everyone had a share in it. The *Kohanim* received some of the meat, the limbs went to the *Mizbeach,* and the man received the remainder of the meat and the skin. Everyone was a partner in it, and everyone received something. That made peace. And it brought blessing to all involved."

"That is fascinating, Mommy. These *korbanos* really have deep meaning. Can you please explain two more things to me?"

"Sure, Chaim."

"I understand how the korban shlamim made peace, but how did it bring blessing? And what is the spiritual vessel that you told me about a few minutes ago?"

"These two points are related to one another, Chaim. A different Midrash explains that the best vessel for holding blessing is peace. Peace is a spiritual vessel. It holds spiritual things, namely blessings. Hashem loves us very much and wants to bless us with all sorts of good things. He wants to give us wisdom, good health, wealth, security, children, and many other good things. However, like the water that you wanted to drink, these blessings must be held inside of something. If not, they will just run away from us and be lost."

"Like the drinking water will spill and be lost without the cup, Mommy?"

"That's right, Chaim."

"Peace is the 'cup' which holds the 'water' of blessings. We have many examples of this in history. When the Jewish people were at peace with one another, they received blessings far greater than could be expected under the circumstances."

"Mommy, what can we do to receive these blessings?"

"We have to be at peace with one another."

"Mommy, you are really great. I ask you for a drink of water, and I receive much more in return. You really know how to make peace."

"That is why I received the greatest blessing of all, Chaim. A wonderful son like you."

> *Kinderlach . . .*
> *Who can think of ways to make peace? "Give in to the other person." "Do not answer back when the other person is angry." "Speak softly." "Communicate clearly." "Don't jump to conclusions." "Judge favorably." "Don't let little things bother you." "Always be the first one to apologize." "Run away from an argument as you would run from a fire." "Work together." "Help other people." "Always try to give more than you get." "Smile, and give compliments whenever you can." These are all correct answers. There are many other answers. Each is a tool. We are making a vessel called peace, and we need to use the proper tools. Kinderlach, may you all make beautiful, big vessels, which Hashem will then fill with blessings.*

Look Carefully

"Chaim, watch yourself. It is slippery over there. Make sure you do not trip."

"No problem Avi, I'm wearing these special traction shoes that . . . oops!"

With that, Chaim slips and falls. The plastic cup that he is carrying falls and breaks. He cuts his finger on the broken cup. The cut is not serious, but still bleeds quite a bit.

"Chaim, are you okay?"

"Yes, I think so. I really should be more careful. These shoes are not as safe as I thought they were."

"Let me give you a bandage to stop the bleeding."

"Thanks so much, Avi. It looks like my broken cup cannot be fixed."

"Count your blessings. It could have been a lot worse. You could have hurt yourself seriously."

Chaim looks at his finger and then the cup. He thinks for a few moments.

"Did you ever wonder why your finger heals and the cup does not, Avi?"

"Honestly, Chaim, I never thought about it."

"Why should the cut skin grow back together? A cut piece of paper does not grow back together."

"I guess you can say that Hashem did us a big favor and made our bodies self-healing. However, He did it in a way that looks so natural that we do not even think about it."

"Avi, you're right. It really is a miracle, but it is hidden in nature. That's the way it was back in the days of the *Beis HaMikdash* (Holy Temple). There were many miracles there, but they were made to look natural."

"Can you give me an example, Chaim?"

"There is one in this week's parasha, Avi. Inside the *Beis HaMikdash* was an altar where the sacrifices were burned. The fire burning those sacrifices was not a natural fire, but a miraculous one that came down from heaven. Still, there was

a mitzvah to make sure there was wood on the fire."

"Why? If Hashem could make a miraculous fire, He could surely make it burn without wood."

"One of our great Rabbis who lived many, many years ago wrote an anonymous book entitled the Sefer HaChinuch. It is a book that explains all of the 613 mitzvos in the Torah. About this mitzvah, he writes that Hashem prefers to run the world according to natural laws. Even when He performs a miracle, He wants to hide it at least partially in the guise of nature. So the fire had to be fed with wood, although it did not really need the wood to burn."

"You know, Chaim, according to what you are saying, there could be miracles happening around us all the time. We just do not recognize them because they are hidden in nature."

"That is exactly what I thought of when I cut my finger, Avi. It is really a miracle that it heals by itself. And what about the birth of a baby?"

"Now that's a real miracle, Chaim. I guess we just have to open our eyes a little wider and look at the world a little more carefully. Then we can see all sorts of wondrous things."

"You're so right, Avi. Not only do I have to watch carefully to avoid falling; I also have to look carefully to see the miracles."

> *Kinderlach . . .*
>
> "Who can think of hidden miracles?" "The rain. It falls in little drops which are just right to water the crops." "Excellent." "The sun. It warms us, lights up the earth, and gives us energy." "Wonderful." "The survival of the Jewish people after the Holocaust. One third of our nation was killed. Almost all of the Torah centers and scholars were wiped out. And now, sixty years later, we have more yeshiva students than ever in history." "That's not a hidden miracle, it is an open one." "May we merit many more."

Parashas Shemini

Soul Building

"It was on the eight day . . ." (*Vayikra* 9:1). This was the eighth day after the seven days of *miluim,* of inaugurating the *Mishkan,* the Tabernacle. For each of the first seven days, Moshe Rabbeinu single-handedly erected the *Mishkan,* offered the sacrifices, and then took down the *Mishkan.* The Divine Presence did not descend. Finally, on the eight day, Aharon HaKohen offered the sacrifices—and the *Shechinah,* the Divine Presence, came to rest upon the *Mishkan.* Then Moshe and Aharon blessed the people. "May the pleasantness of Hashem our God be upon us; and may the work of our hands be fixed upon us; and may He make the work of our hands permanent" (*Tehillim* 90:17).

The Malbim explains that Hashem takes pleasure, so to speak, when His creations fulfill their intended purpose. We were created to perform His mitzvos properly. When we do that, He takes pleasure in us. He continues to explain that when a person builds a house, it may be beautiful, strong, and comfortable, but it is not a part of the person. It is outside of him. The blessing is that our handiwork should become a part of us. When a person does a mitzvah, it becomes fixed in his soul. It becomes a part of his character and is with him forever. Lastly, we are blessed that Hashem should make all of our handiwork a permanent part of us. All of our deeds should be good in His eyes; therefore, He will fix them within our souls.

> *Kinderlach . . .*
> *People build all sorts of things. Some have hobbies building model cars, boats, or planes. Some people build buildings. Some exercise to build up their bodies. The blessing of Moshe and Aharon tells us to build up our souls by doing mitzvos properly. Soul building is important for two reasons. Number one, it lasts forever. Longer than the biggest, tallest, strongest building. More importantly, it gives Hashem pleasure. That is the greatest thing that we can do.*

Rotten Bones

"Shalom, Mommy, I'm home."

"Shalom, Devora. How was school?"

"Not so good."

"I'm sorry to hear that. Let me make you a hot drink and we'll sit down and talk about it."

"Thanks, Mommy."

Devora sips on the sweet hot chocolate and begins to talk.

"It's that girl who sits in front of me in class."

"What did she do?"

"We had a spelling contest and she won. I studied so hard for that contest. I wanted to win."

"Devora, no effort is ever wasted. I'm sure your spelling has improved tremendously."

"But Mommy, she always wins."

"What do you mean?"

"She gets the best grades on her report card. She has the most friends. She has the nicest clothes. She has wonderful *middos* (character traits). She is just perfect. I'm so jealous of her."

"Devora dear, I doubt very much that she is perfect. However, even if she is, that is no reason to be jealous of her. Jealousy is a very bad *middah*. Shlomo HaMelech, the wisest of all men, wrote: 'Jealousy rots the bones' (*Mishlei* 14:30). Our Sages added to this by saying, "Jealousy, desire, and honor take a person out of the (real) world" (*Pirkei Avos* 4:21). The Mesillas Yesharim explains that a person gains nothing from jealousy. It does not make him any better nor his friend any worse."

"You're so right, Mommy."

"Devora, we must all work on our *bitachon* (trust) in Hashem. He provides us with everything we need. Our friend has what she needs. If you do not have what she has, that means that you do not need it. Therefore, why be jealous? Would you be jealous of a baby's dress which is ten sizes too small for you?"

"Of course not. It's not for me."

"You friend's dress, which might happen to fit you, is not for you either."

"Thank you so much, Mommy. I am going to focus on thanking Hashem for what He has given me. I am so fortunate."

"So am I, Devora. To have a daughter like you."

"A fire came forth from before Hashem and consumed them (Nadav and Avihu, the sons of Aharon HaKohen), and they died before Hashem" (*Vayikra* 10:2). What was the sin that caused their deaths? One interpretation is: Nadav and Avihu walked behind Moshe and Aharon saying, "When will these two elders die? Then we will rule this nation" (*Sanhedrin* 52a). The Maharsha comments that their sin was jealousy.

Kinderlach . . .

"He got a new toy and I didn't." He needed one and you did not. "She got two cookies and I only got one." She worked harder to earn them. "She has more friends than I do." She is outgoing and talks to everyone; you are more quiet but your friends are very close ones. "He runs faster than I do." True, but you think faster than he does. Hashem gave you each your own special talents. Your job is to work with what you have. Don't be jealous of the other one. You have everything you need to be the best possible you.

It's Hard For Me

"Avi, it's time to get up."

"Oh. Already? But I just went to sleep, Abba."

"Believe it or not, you went to sleep eight hours ago. Now it is time to begin your day."

"But it's so hard for me to get out of bed."

"I know. I empathize with you. Let me tell you about Aharon HaKohen. It was hard for him to carry out a mitzvah also. He had to approach the Holy Altar and perform the Divine service. The Imrei Emes relates that this is the way of the *yetzer hara* (evil inclination). He makes mitzvos seem difficult. However, the point goes deeper than that."

"Really?"

"We were sent down to this earth to perfect ourselves. Each one of us has his own *middos* that need work. How do we know which areas we have to work on?"

"The ones which are the most difficult for us?"

"Excellent. The *yetzer hara* makes the most important things seem the most difficult."

"That is such an important thought, Abba!"

"Use it well, Avi, and overcome that evil *yetzer hara*."

Kinderlach . . .
What is your job in this world? What middos *were you sent here to work on? Just think about which are the most difficult for you. Is it hard for you to get up in the morning? How about speaking quietly; is that difficult? We all have our challenges. Difficult mitzvos and* middos *need work. That is your job in life.*

Parashas Tazria

The Projectile

"We have now reached the final session of your training program. Please step this way."

The trainees moved in closer to see the giant missile, standing on its underground launch pad.

"This missile is deadly. Its warhead can cause untold destruction."

"Sir, what triggers the launch of this missile?"

"That is a very good question, young man. It is voice activated. It has a sound sensor that identifies certain words. If they are spoken, the missile blasts off."

"Sir, is it confidential information to ask what is the destination of this missile?"

"It is very confidential, because no one knows its destination."

"What? It could be pointed at my home town!"

"That's right."

"If I say one of the code words, I could activate the missile and destroy many people."

"Young man, you are right. You had better watch what you say."

> *Kinderlach . . .*
> *Do you recognize this parable? The code words are lashon hara, and the missile is the destruction that it causes. The Chafetz Chaim in his book "Shmiras HaLashon" describes what happens when we speak lashon hara. The words go up to heaven, and evil forces grab hold of them. They send them back down to earth in the form of death and destruction. We must be very careful what we say, for every word is heard, and comes back to haunt us.*

What A Welcome

"Come forward, please. We have been expecting you."

The man stepped forward nervously. He had never been here before, and did not know what to expect.

"Yes, after 120 years of doing mitzvos, you have finally arrived. Now is the time to receive your reward."

The man felt comforted. He had performed many mitzvos in his life. Perhaps it would be okay after all.

"First, let us hear about your life. The angels have recorded all of your deeds. Let them come forward and tell us about you."

A huge door swung open and revealed thousands of angels ready to speak about this man.

"On the 12th of Teves, he spoke badly about his neighbor."

"On the 13th of Teves, he degraded his relative."

The man's heart began to drop. These angels heard all of the lashon hara that he had said. Every word was a separate sin.

"Excuse me. I am so sorry, but may I interrupt for a second?"

"Go ahead."

"How many angels are here, recounting my *lashon hara*?"

"That is a good question. Let us figure it out. You spoke many words every day. You learned Torah; you conducted your business and personal affairs. You probably spoke no more that four or five words of *lashon hara* each day."

"Probably. That is not very many."

"Let's add them up. Four or five words a day, is about thirty words a week. Multiply that by fifty-two weeks of the year and you have about 1,500 words per year. By the age of 68 (which is 55 years after your bar mitzvah) you have accumulated 80,000 words of *lashon hara*."

The man began to cry.

"Oh, what have I done. How I have misused my power of speech. If I had only known this while I was alive. Now it is too late."

> *Kinderlach* . . .
> The Chafetz Chaim makes this simple calculation in his book "Shmiras HaLashon." Our words are never forgotten. They are stored in Hashem's computer (so to speak). Even a few words a day add up. Every day, another few words of lashon hara, until the numbers are very large. Now is the time to stop while we can. Learn the laws of lashon hara and stop yourself from speaking badly about people. Turn off the calculator today.

Keep Them Pure

We return to our scene of the man in heaven. He is stating the case in his favor, even though he has spoken many words of loshon hora.

"But I learned Torah. I prayed to Hashem with *kavannah* (concentration). What about those holy words that I spoke? Don't they speak well for me? Can they not counter the words of *lashon hara*?"

"Let us examine your wares. You are claiming that your holy words are beautiful produce. Like the merchant who comes to the market with bushels of apples. When he picked them from the tree, they were beautiful, fresh, and clean. When he arrives at the market and uncovers them, he finds them all dirty, spoiled, and rotten."

"What happened?"

"The good apples became mixed with bad, dirty ones, and they spoiled the whole lot."

"What are you telling me about my words of Torah learning and prayer?"

"They are not as clean and pure as you thought. The spiritual dirt and impurity that you have created by speaking *lashon hara* has stuck to your holy words of Torah and made them impure. They no longer have the same power to speak well for you. Your reward for them has diminished greatly."

"*Oy va voy*. All of those years that I learned Torah. All of those beautiful words. Ruined, spoiled, and contaminated!"

"I am sorry."

Kinderlach . . .

Learning Torah is the greatest mitzvah. As the Mishnah states, "Talmud Torah is equivalent to all of them." However, words of Torah will be ruined by lashon hara. Imagine someone who spends his whole life working on something, only to find it ruined in the end. What a tragedy. Don't let this happen to you. Practice Shmiras HaLoshon . . . now.

Parashas Metzora

The Craftsman

"Look at this shop. There are beautiful wood objects in the window. Let's go inside."

"Sure."

Inside the shop they find a carpenter working on building a wooden table. His skilled hands patiently work the wood, carving out beautiful shapes.

"Yes, can I help you?"

"We were just admiring your work. Your wooden creations are beautiful."

"I have been working with wood since I was eight years old. I have the finest tools at my disposal. Still, I must measure every cut that I make very carefully. The smallest mistake will ruin the whole piece."

"Craftsmanship seems to be a lifelong endeavor."

"It certainly is."

"What is a person's profession in this world? To make himself like a mute." (*Chullin* 89a). A mute person cannot speak. The Gemara is telling us that a person should learn how to be quiet, as a mute is. Learn how to be quiet? What learning is required? Anyone can close his or her mouth. Or can they?

The Chafetz Chaim explains that silence is a profession. A truly excellent craftsman learns his trade at a very young age. It becomes second nature to him. He can approach even the hardest jobs calmly, with the skill necessary to complete them. So too with silence. A person should train himself from the youngest age.

Learn to control your speech. Measure every word carefully, as the craftsman measures each cut of the saw blade. Then, when you are placed in a testing situation, you will have the tools necessary to be quiet and not speak *lashon hara*. You will be a true craftsman.

Kinderlach . . .

The Trickster

"Please, my friend, come. You look like you are a stranger in town."

The stranger was very happy to be welcomed by such a friendly individual. He indeed was visiting in town and needed a place to eat and stay. Little did he know that his "friend" was really a trickster.

"Come, please let me show you around town and help you get settled. I will arrange a place for you to sleep tonight. But first, I am sure that you are hungry. Please, come with me for a bite to eat."

The trickster proceeded to take the stranger to a fancy restaurant. They entered and were shown to their seats.

"Please order whatever you like," said the trickster. "I will pay for everything. We will work out the bill some other time."

The items listed on the menu all sounded delicious and were very expensive. "This man is very generous," thought the stranger. "It is my good fortune that I met him."

The two men proceeded to order a sumptuous meal, complete from soup to dessert. The food was served with all of its courses, and they enjoyed themselves tremendously. As they finished eating and drinking, the trickster excused himself for a few minutes. He slipped away out the back door of the restaurant. The waiter then came and presented the guest with a huge bill.

"Yes, just a moment. My host will be returning to pay this."

They waited and waited, but the trickster was nowhere to be found. The owner of the restaurant came to help the waiter.

"But, but, my friend was supposed to pay this bill," the man pleaded.

"Your friend is not here, but you are. You ate this food and must pay for it."

The guest, realizing that he had been tricked, sadly took out his wallet and paid the expensive bill for the meal.

Kinderlach . . .

This is a parable from the Chafetz Chaim. What is the message? While the guest was eating, he thought the trickster was his friend. It was only after the meal that he realized that he was only out to harm him. So too with lashon hara. Someone may want to tell you the deepest secrets that he knows about other people. How honored and flattered you feel that he considers you so close a friend that he wants to share such secrets with you. However, after 120 years we will see that your closeness to such a person caused you to hear lashon hara. That "friendship," just like the meal at the restaurant, will cause you a great loss. Don't let the trickster fool you. Be smart and stay away from "friends" like the trickster.

Parashas Acharei Mos

No Exceptions to the Rule

"Come, Avi—hurry. We'll be late for class!"

"Relax, Chaim. We still have two minutes until the school bell rings."

"I know, but it's a five minute walk from here to the school gate."

"What are you worried about? We'll be three minutes late. What is so terrible about that?"

"There are two reasons why I want to be there on time. First of all, three minutes of Torah learning is very precious, Avi. I could make up the loss by staying later after class, but the second reason is what I am really worried about: the school's new rule."

"What rule is that, Chaim?"

"Didn't you hear? The school gate will be closed one minute after the bell rings. If you come late you will be locked out."

"That can't be. How do they expect people to keep to that rule?"

"Apparently, a lot of time has been lost due to lateness. The principal wants to put a stop to it. That's why he passed this rule. So let's hurry and make it on time before the gate closes."

"You go right ahead, Chaim. I'm not worried if I get there a few minutes late. It's only the first day of the new rule. They are bound to be lenient. And even if they are not, I am still not worried. I'm not bragging, but I am one of the best students in the class. I am always careful about things like this. I am sure that this rule was not made for people like me. It was made for the weaker students who either need the extra learning-time or who have made a habit of coming late."

"Okay, Avi. It's your choice."

"I'll see you in class, Chaim."

"I hope so."

With that, Chaim runs ahead toward the school. Just as the bell rings, he reaches the school gate panting and out of breath. Sure enough, one minute after the bell the gate is locked. Avi and a few other latecomers come to the gate, asking the guard to open it.

"I'm sorry, boys, I can't open the gate today. Didn't you hear about the new rule?"

"But please, can't you make an exception just this one time?"

"The principal gave me strict orders, boys. No exceptions to the rules."

"Sir, may I please speak to the principal?"

"You want to speak to the principal? That's asking a lot, young man."

"I know, but I have a good reason. Can you please call him on the phone?"

"Okay, young man. What is your name?"

"Avi."

"Hello, Rabbi Cohen. Yes, it's Shlomo, the guard at the gate. There is a young man here named Avi who wants to speak with you."

"Young man, the principal is on the phone. He will speak with you."

Avi takes the phone and begins speaking with Rabbi Cohen.

"Rabbi Cohen, I found out about the new rule today on the way to school. I came to school about three minutes late and am locked out. I understand why the new rule was made, but I feel that the Rabbi can make an exception for me today. After all, the rule was made for weaker students and habitual latecomers. Not for someone like me. Correct?"

"Avi, you are an excellent student, Baruch Hashem. Please tell me how this week's parasha begins."

"Hashem spoke to Moshe after the death of the two sons of Aharon."

"Excellent, Avi. Usually the Torah writes, 'Hashem spoke to Moshe saying.' Why this time does it write 'after the death of the two sons of Aharon?'"

"I often wondered about that, Rabbi Cohen."

"Rabbi Chaim Ben Attar, the great sage who wrote a commentary on the Torah entitled the 'Ohr HaChaim,' answers this question. This verse is directed toward Moshe Rabbeinu – the man who came closest to Hashem. He is called 'Hashem's trusted one,' who is able to enter the holy section of the Mishkan. He is the greatest prophet who ever lived. Still, he should not think that his closeness to Hashem allows him to break the rules. The sons of Aharon were 'krovim' (of close relationship) to Hashem. Still, that did not help them. When they broke the rules, they had to suffer the consequences. Hashem was teaching Moshe that a close relationship does not allow one to break the rules. So you see, Avi, the rules were not made to be broken. Although you are an excellent student, and we are very close, you must still obey the rules."

"I understand, Rabbi Cohen. The most important rule to learn is that there are no exceptions to the rules."

"100%, Avi. May Hashem always guide you along the straight path, with no exceptions to the rule."

Kinderlach . . .

The rules were made to be followed, not broken. The bad trait of self-pride is what makes us want to break the rules. "I am important. I can break the rules. I am different." That is the yetzer hara talking. Let's beat that yetzer hara by always following all of the rules. No exceptions.

Parashas Kedoshim

The List

"Avi, I can't handle this list."

"What list, Chaim?"

"The list of negative mitzvos from this week's parasha. 'Do not steal, do not deal falsely, do not lie, do not swear falsely, do not cheat, do not rob, pay on time, do not curse, do not mislead, do not gossip, do not stand idly by, do not hate your brother, do not take revenge, and do not bear a grudge' (*Vayikra* 19:11–18). How can a person even remember all of these things?"

"Chaim, you are right. It is a long list. We have to be very sensitive to our fellow Jews. We must not do anything to hurt them in any way."

"Do you have any advice to help me, Avi?"

"Read the next words of the verse."

"'You shall love your fellow Jew as yourself, I am Hashem.' How does this help me?"

"The Sefer HaChinuch explains that this mitzvah is the key. Rebbe Akiva relates in the Sifra that this is a fundamental principle of the Torah. Many mitzvos of the Torah are tied into it. One who loves his friend like himself would not steal his money, trick him, insult him, or take business from him underhandedly. He would not harm him in any way. This is something that anyone can understand."

"What you are saying, Avi, is that if I focus on loving my friend, then everything else falls into place."

"Exactly."

> Kinderlach . . .
> You have to keep your eye on the ball. Don't get confused or distracted. The yetzer hara wants to convince you that it is too hard to keep all of these mitzvos. Really it is a piece of cake. Just keep one thing in mind: love your friend. The rest is easy.

Like Yourself

"Okay, Avi. You convinced me. I have to love him like myself. That means that I must therefore love myself. If I don't, then I can't love him."

"I never considered that, Chaim, but you are right. If you are commanded to love your fellow Jew like yourself, then you must love yourself first, in order to love him like yourself."

"Right. The next question is, 'How do you love yourself?'"

"That's a good question, Chaim. I guess someone can love himself because he is smart, or because he is a good athlete."

"That is true, but before long he will meet someone who is smarter or more athletic than he is. Or he might injure himself and not be able to play sports anymore. Does he love himself less, or stop loving himself?"

"No, of course not. His love must be based on something deeper."

"Right. The deepest, most important thing about a person is that Hashem created him, in His image. He is connected to Hashem who is always watching over him."

"Wow. When we realize how important we are, that creates a deep love."

"Exactly. Hashem loves us. How can we not love ourselves?"

"And the same is true about our friend. Hashem also created him and loves him. Therefore we see how important he is, and we love him."

Kinderlach . . .

A child who receives the love that he needs from his parents feels safe and secure. Because his parents love him, he loves himself. The Jewish people are Hashem's special children. He loves us as a parent loves his children. Therefore, we love him just as we love Daddy and Mommy. And we love ourselves. Then, we move on to the next step: loving others.

Giving Brings Love

"Avi, the Torah is so beautiful. It tells us that we have to love ourselves, and that we have to love others like ourselves. You explained to me how to love ourselves and others. I have just one problem."

"What's that, Chaim?"

"I know that I am supposed to love my fellow Jew, but I just don't feel it in my heart, and I am not used to it."

"Chaim, the Torah has a solution for that also. In Vayikra 19:9–10, the Torah commands us not to harvest the corner of the field, rather to leave it for poor people. Similarly, what falls to the ground during the harvest is left to those in need."

"I understand that we have to give to them, Avi. But what does that have to do with loving them?"

"Rav Dessler explains that giving leads to love. If you want to develop feelings of love toward someone, help him. Give to him. Do favors for him. You will be drawn after your actions and your feelings for him will awaken. The greatest proof of this is parents and children. Everyone in this world has two people who are madly in love with him. His mother and his father. Why? Because they constantly give to him from the beginning moment of his life. This giving brings about a deep love that lasts a lifetime."

Kinderlach . . .

It all ties together. Hashem loves us. Therefore, we love ourselves. Therefore, we love our fellow Jews. He commands us to help them and give to them, in order to awaken and strengthen that love. Doing anything bad to them becomes unthinkable. Kinderlach, we should all be very successful in loving ourselves and all of our fellow Jews.

Parashas Emor

Mr. Ambassador

"Chaim, this train is sure filling up fast."

"Baruch Hashem we got these seats near the front, while the train was almost empty, Avi."

At the next stop, a man struggling with his many packages walks up the steps of the train. Chaim and Avi quickly rise and give him their seats on the train.

"Thank you so much, boys. That was so nice of you. It is comforting to see such well-mannered young men."

"Thank you very much, sir."

"Do you mind if I ask you a personal question, boys?"

"Not at all, sir."

"What are those little round hats that you are wearing on your heads?"

"They are called *kippot*, sir."

"Why do you wear them?"

"We are religious Jews and we cover our heads to remind ourselves that there is a Higher Power above us."

"Really! Where did you learn such a thing?"

"It is in our Torah, sir."

"Boys, I myself am Jewish. I never had much of a Jewish education, so I don't know much about the Torah. Tell me something else that is in the Torah."

"Well, sir, when we gave you our seat, we fulfilled at least three commandments."

"There are ten commandments altogether, correct?"

"Not exactly. Those ten that you are thinking of are very important because they were the first ones given on Mt. Sinai. However, there are a total of 613 commandments in the Torah."

"Which three did you fulfill?"

"First, 'Love your fellow Jew as yourself' (Vayikra 19:18). Whenever we perform an act of kindness to a fellow Jew, we fulfill this commandment. Second, 'Rise in the presence of an older person' (Vayikra 19:32). We stood up to show our respect for someone older than ourselves. Third, sanctification of Hashem's Name (Vayikra 22:32)."

"Boys, those first two commandments are wonderful! They show how you really care for other people and respect them. You boys are very fortunate that you learned these things from the Torah. It is a pleasure to be with you because you are so refined. Now, what is that last commandment?"

"Believe it or not, sir, that last commandment is to be a proper representative of Hashem and the Torah. The Talmud states your words almost exactly. One who fulfills the Torah's teachings causes people to say about him, 'Fortunate are his father and his teacher who taught him Torah. Oy to those who do not learn Torah! Look how his ways are delightful, his deeds are refined.' You see, sir, we are all Hashem's ambassadors. People are observing us. They judge Hashem and the Torah by our actions. When we behave properly, we cause people to say nice things about Hashem. That is one way that we fulfill the commandment of sanctifying His Name."

"Boys, you are both worthy emissaries. I would like very much to meet your teacher. Perhaps he could teach me Torah."

"Why not? Then you can become a representative too! The Jewish people are always looking for good ambassadors. Please follow us. Your limousine is waiting, sir. VIP's get the red carpet treatment!"

Kinderlach . . .

People are watching us. We are representatives of Hashem. On the train, they are watching to see if we give up our seat for an older person. At the store, they are watching to see if we wait patiently for our turn. At the playground, they are watching to see if we play nicely and do not litter. They look to see if our clothes are neat and clean. When they speak to us, they notice if we listen and answer politely or not. You have many opportunities to be shining examples of how Hashem and His Torah can refine a person. Let us take turns around the Shabbos table trying to think of other examples. Maybe we can even ask Daddy to give a prize to the one who thinks of the most examples.

The City of Happiness

"I am really exhausted," the man thought to himself. "I had such a hard day at work this Erev Shabbos. I hope I have enough strength to concentrate on my prayers when I get to shul. Oy, am I tired. How am I going to conduct the Shabbos table? Will I have enough patience for the children? What will I do if they don't behave? I know… when I walk in the door, I will tell everyone how I feel, and ask them to please be sympathetic. Hmmm. Will that really work? It does not sound too promising. Little children cannot behave perfectly the whole evening. Oy, what will I do?"

The prayers finished and the man begins walking home. The crisp cool night air fills his lungs. He takes a few deep breaths, and speaks to himself.

"I am so fortunate. Hashem has given me a beautiful family. They are all waiting for me to come home with a smile on my face, to begin the Shabbos table."

His mood begins to perk up.

"I have my health. I have a good livelihood. We have such nice neighbors."

He takes more deep breaths, gaining strength with every step.

"We live in a beautiful neighborhood. I have time to learn Torah. I have a good *chavrusa* (study partner). Hashem is so good to me. How can I be in a bad mood?"

The man reaches the front door of house. He knocks, then opens the door with a big smile on his face.

"Good Shabbos, everyone!"

"Good Shabbos, Daddy!"

"These are Hashem's appointed times" (*Vayikra* 23:4). The Torah goes on to describe the cycle of the Jewish year, with its festivals and many special mitzvos. Later, in Parashas Re'eh (*Devarim* 16:14–15), the Torah lists more mitzvos relating to the holy days. "You shall be happy on your festival . . . you will be completely happy." We have a mitzvah that commands us to be happy. Can this be? Can the Torah obligate us to control our moods and frame of mind? Yet the Torah does—it must be possible. Hashem never expects from us what we cannot do.

Rav Eliezer Papo wrote a book entitled "Pele Yo'etz." He mentions techniques for bringing a person to a state of happiness. Imagine that you just found a huge sum of money. Would anything interfere with your joy? When you are learning Torah and doing mitzvos, you are receiving a reward that is far, far greater than all the money in the world. At these times you should be elated! What if you were saved from a threat of certain death? Your joy would be endless. How happy you would be to thank the person who saved you. Hashem brings you your food every day. Without it you would surely perish. How thrilled you should be to thank Him when saying your blessings. His gifts are endless.

Kinderlach . . .
Don't wait around for happiness to come to you. Go get it. Make a list of ten things that give you pleasure. Mommy's delicious cooking. Mommy's warm smile and hug. Getting 100% on a test. Going on a nice vacation. Making Hashem happy. Don't you feel happier already? It's all up to you. Remember that the City of Happiness is in the "state" of mind.

Parashas Behar

Costly Words

"This is a beautiful gift shop, sir."

"Thank you very much, young man."

"Sir, may I ask you how much this tallis costs?"

"That tallis is all wool and it costs sixty dollars, young man."

"Thank you very much, sir. How much does this shofar cost?"

"That shofar is a very special one. It costs thirty-five dollars."

"I see. And how about this menorah? Is it real silver?"

"No, it is only silver plated, young man."

"How much does it cost?"

"I will sell that to you for fifty dollars, young man."

"That seems like a good price. How much is this mezuzah cover?"

"You can have it for ten dollars, young man."

"Thank you very much for answering all of my questions, sir. Do you mind if I ask you one more price?"

"Not at all, young man. May I ask you something first?"

"Sure."

"Do you intend on buying any of these things?"
"Ummm. Well. Uh. Not really."

"I hope I didn't make you feel bad by asking. I don't mind answering all of your questions. I will tell you the price of everything in the store if you like. I just want to teach you a *halachah* (Jewish law)."
"Which *halachah* is that, sir?"
"The *halachah* that forbids *onaas devarim*."
"What is *onaas devarim?* It sounds pretty serious."

"It is, young man. Rav Yisrael Meir Kagan, known to us by the name of his famous book, Chafetz Chaim, writes about *onaas devarim* in the opening chapter of his book. The source of this law is actually a verse in this week's parasha. 'You shall not cause your fellow Jew aggravation' (*Vayikra* 25:17). Any words that will cause distress to a fellow Jew—that will anger him, scare him, embarrass him, or cause him pain—fall into the category of *onaas devarim*."

"Did I say something wrong, sir?"
"The Mishnah (*Bava Metzia* 4:10) lists examples of *onaas devarim*. It states, 'Do not ask the price of an object if you do not intend to buy.' This seems like a very minor thing to us. But the Mishnah is telling us how sensitive we must be to others' feelings. The storekeeper may be busy, or tired, or just not feel like answering questions."
"Do our Sages list any other examples of *onaas devarim?*"

"Yes, there are a few. Do not remind a person of sins that he committed in the past. Do not ask someone a question that you know he cannot answer. Do not give someone bad advice or false directions."

"I never realized that these things were forbidden."

"That is why I told you, young man. The Torah teaches us that our words are very powerful. A slip of the tongue can embarrass someone, hurt their feelings, or even make them cry. So much aggravation and even hatred can be avoided by thinking carefully before we speak. On the other hand, a kind word of appreciation or encouragement can lift a person's spirits. Compliments have changed people's whole lives."

"Sir, you corrected me in such a gentle way that I actually feel good about it. You are very careful with your speech."

"What is your name, young man?"

"Avi, sir."

"Avi, the Torah tells us that we should only correct a person if we think he will be able to receive it. I saw from the minute you entered the store that you are a fine young man. When you made the mistake, I just knew that you would be interested in improving yourself."

"Sir, we should both have only good things to say about each other."

"Avi, I think you realize that your words are more valuable than anything in this store."

"And I won't even ask you how much they cost, sir."

> *Kinderlach . . .*
> *Every word can be a gem. A word of Torah is equal to all 613 mitzvos combined. There is no gem more valuable than that. A word of comfort can lift a person's spirits. Priceless. A word of encouragement can lead to worlds of accomplishment. Use your worlds carefully. They are more valuable than you can imagine.*

Shmitta

"Yaakov, may I water our garden during the Shmitta year?"

"Yes, Rachel. We live here in Eretz Yisrael and we are observing the Shmitta, but you may water it enough to keep the grass alive."

"How do I know how much water it needs to stay alive?"

"Experiment and see. If you see it drying out too much then water it."

"That may not be so easy."

"Do your best, Rachel dear, and Hashem will help."

Rachel did her best, but most of the grass withered and died. The garden, which had been lush and green, was now mostly dirt.

"Now that the Shmitta is over, what shall we do about the garden, Yaakov?"

"I phoned a gardener, and he wants a lot of money to plant new grass."

"Oy, I feel so badly that I let it all die."

"Don't feel bad, Rachel. You observed Shmitta. That is more important than the grass. Let us wait until after the winter to phone the gardener. We don't use the garden much during the winter, anyway."

That winter brought great blessings of rain to Eretz Yisrael. Yaakov and Rachel watched in elation as their garden began to sprout with beautiful green grass. By the end of the winter, all the grass had grown back. "When you come into the Land that I give you, the Land shall observe a Shabbos rest for Hashem" (Vayikra 25:2).

"Yaakov, look at our beautiful garden."

"A gift from Hashem."

Kinderlach . . .

The Torah promises that those who observe Shmitta will never lose. The same is true about honoring Shabbos, Yom Tov, lending to poor people, and giving tsedaka. Keeping the Torah is the best investment. You never lose!

Parashas Bechukosai

Are You Listening?

"Mr. Eisen, your stockbroker is on the phone."

"Yes, Harry. Con-Am Inc. is up three points? Sell 20,000 shares."

"Mr. Eisen, your real estate broker is on the phone."

"Yes Jack. The building permit just went through? Build 1000 more units."

"Mr. Eisen, your attorney is on the phone."

"Yes, Jeremy. They want a settlement? Okay. Nothing less than $250,000."

"Mr. Eisen, your son is on the phone."

"Yes, Moishe. What?????"

Mr. Eisen grabs his jacket and flies out of the office. He drops all of his business matters to attend to his son.

"If you will follow My decrees and observe My commandments and perform them, then I will provide your rains in their time. And the land will give its produce, and the tree of the field will give its fruit. . . . I will turn My attention to you, I will make you fruitful and increase you" (Vayikra 26:3–9). Rashi explains "I will turn to you": Hashem will turn aside from all of His occupations, so to speak, in order to give you reward. He will bestow bountiful blessings on His Nation, when we keep His mitzvos.

"But if you will not listen to Me and will not perform all of these commandments . . . I will do the same to you. I will designate terror upon you . . . I will turn My attention against you and you will be struck down before your enemies" (*Vayikra* 26:14–17). Rashi explains "I will turn My attention against you": Hashem will turn aside from all of His occupations, so to speak, to give punishment to the Jewish people.

In our story, Mr. Eisen dropped all of his business affairs to attend to his son. He turned his full attention to him. Just as Hashem turns His attention to us. This shows his great love and concern for his son. Equally great is Hashem's love and concern for the Jewish people.

Kinderlach . . .
This parasha illustrates Hashem's great love for us. He drops everything that He is doing (so to speak) to attend to us. We are more important to Him than all of His other affairs. Doesn't that make you feel great? You are so important, and Hashem loves you so much. With that privilege comes responsibility, though. We must listen to Him. When we listen, He showers us with blessings. When we don't listen, oy va voy. When we suffer at the hands of our enemies, we must ask ourselves, "Are we listening?"

Keep Your Word

"Chaim, I really want to continue learning with you, but I must stop now."

"Why is that, Avi?"

"Because I must go to a bar mitzvah."

"I would also like to continue learning a little longer."

"It is wonderful that we enjoy learning together. However, my friend Jack told me that he would meet me at the bus stop at 8:00 to travel to the bar mitzvah."

"Okay, Avi. Please wish a mazel tov from me."

Avi hurries to the bus stop. The 8:00 bus arrives, and Jack is not there. The 8:15 and 8:30 buses also pass. Finally, he gets on the 8:45 bus without Jack. He arrives at the bar mitzvah 45 minutes late. He finds a pay phone and calls Jack.

"Hello, Jack, this is Avi."

"Avi, where are you?"

"I am at the bar mitzvah. I waited for you at the bus stop."

"Oh, I'm so sorry, Avi. Something came up and I forgot to call you. I hope that I did not cause you any inconvenience."

"That's okay Jack."

Avi stays a while at the bar mitzvah, then heads home.

"Hi Daddy, I'm home."

"Great to see you, Avi. You are a little late. We were beginning to worry."

"I'm okay, Daddy. We had a little communication problem. Someone changed his plans and did not inform me. I waited for him for 45 minutes."

"I see."

"I really learned an important lesson tonight, Daddy."

"What's that, Avi?"

"How important it is to keep your word."

"How timely, Avi."

"Why, Daddy?"

"Because keeping your word is one of the subjects of this week's parasha. Parashas Bechukosai speaks about *nedarim*. vows (*Vayikra* 27). *Nedarim* are a very serious matter. The Gemara (*Nedarim* 22a) teaches that making a vow is like building a forbidden altar. Fulfilling the vow is like offering a sacrifice on that altar."

"Wow."

"The Pele Yo'etz writes that terrible punishments will come to one who makes a *neder*."

"Daddy, what is considered a *neder*?"

"That is a good question, Avi. If we look in the text of the *Hataras Nedarim* (Annulment of Vows) that we say each Erev Rosh Hashanah, we find that even promises to do good deeds need annulment. We have to realize that our words are important."

"Right, Daddy. People are depending on us to fulfill what we say. I was left waiting at the bus stop for 45 minutes, instead of learning with Chaim, because someone did not keep his word."

"That is correct, Avi. It goes even deeper. Hashem also hears every word that we say and takes note of all of our actions. Therefore, the Pele Yo'etz has some good advice for us. Develop the habit of saying 'bli neder' (without a vow) whenever you say that you will do something. That way you have not made a commitment. You should still try your hardest to fulfill what you say. After all, people are depending on you. Saying 'bli neder' will make you realize the seriousness of your words, and at the same time save you from punishment for *nedarim*."

"Thank you, Daddy. I really learned a lesson. From now on I will always try my best to keep my word."

"And just to be on the safe side, always say 'bli neder' as well.

"Bli neder."

Kinderlach . . .

Take your words seriously. Do not commit yourself unless you are confident that you can keep your word. Remember that people are counting on you. A trustworthy person is a pillar of society. People can count on what he says. He also gains self-confidence. He knows his limits. He makes sure to keep his commitments. Become a trusted person. Keep your word.

Simcha's Kinder Torah

Sefer Bamidbar

Parashas Bamidbar

The Center

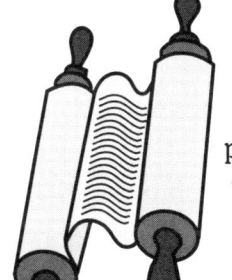

"That model looks really neat, Chaim. What is it?"

"It is a model of the camp of the Jewish people during the years in the desert, Avi. The twelve tribes are camped around the outside. Inside is the camp of the *Kohanim* and *Leviim*."

"What is that in the center?"

"That is the *Mishkan* (Tabernacle)."

"What is inside the *Mishkan*?"

"Many things. The holiest part is the *Kodesh Kodoshim* (Holy of Holies)."

"What is inside of the *Kodesh Kodoshim*?"

"The *Aron HaKodesh* (Holy Ark)."

"Do you mind if I ask you one more question, Chaim?"

"Not at all, Avi."

"What is inside of the *Aron HaKodesh*?"

"That's a good question, Avi. Inside of the *Aron HaKodesh* is the *Sefer Torah*."

"Why is that such a good question, Chaim?"

"Because now you have come to the very center. The *Sefer Torah* is in the innermost part of the camp. It is inside the *Aron HaKodesh*, which is inside the *Kodesh Kodoshim*, which is inside the *Mishkan*, which is inside the camp of the *Kohanim* and *Leviim*, which is inside of the camp of the twelve tribes."

"I see why my question was good. Hashem does not do anything haphazardly, and He must have had a very good reason for instructing the Jewish people to set up the camp this way. The center of a community is its focal point and should contain something or someone very important."

"Exactly, Avi. The Chafetz Chaim explains why the *Sefer Torah* was in the center. Also in our synagogues nowadays, the *Sefer Torah* is read on the *bimah*, a table in the center of the shul. Similarly, the *Eitz HaChaim* (Tree of Life) was planted in the center of the Garden of Eden. This all a beautiful parable to the Torah, which is our 'Tree of Life.'

"The human body is also involved in the parable. The life force flows from the heart. Therefore, it is in the center of the body. It pumps the blood, which carries this life force to all parts of the body, and they all receive their energy from it. So you see, when Hashem designs something, He puts its energy source right in the center."

"The Torah must be the energy source for the Jewish people, Chaim."

"Right again, Avi. The Torah is the generator of the spiritual energy that keeps us alive. In the last blessing of the *Amidah* prayer, the Torah is referred to as '*Toras Chaim*,' the Torah of Life."

"We had better get busy, Chaim."

"Doing what?"

"If Hashem Himself put the Torah in the center of the camp, then we must surely put it in the center of our lives."

Kinderlach . . .

The Torah is called our Torah of life because it guides us how to live our lives. Everything that we do should revolve around it. The halachah *(Torah law) guides us in all areas. It tells us how to eat, how to speak, how to conduct our business matters, and how to treat our family, friends, and neighbors. Whenever we think about doing something, our first question must be, "How should this be done according to Torah?" There is a right and a wrong way to do everything. The Torah tells us the right way.*

Your Number

"Sir, how much do these potatoes cost?"

"Three shekels per kilo."

"How many potatoes are in this sack?"

"I don't know, young man. I sell the potatoes by weight, not by number."

"You don't know how many potatoes you have in these sacks?"

"Not really."

"Can I ask you a personal question, sir?"

"Go right ahead, young man."

"How many children do you have?"

"Eight."

"You know how many children you have, but you don't know how many potatoes you have?"

"Young man, there is a bit of a difference. Every child is a person. A whole world. Each one needs my personal attention and supervision to grow up to be a normal, productive person. Potatoes are just potatoes. Although they are different shapes and weights, we eat them all just the same."

"Take a census of the entire assembly of the Children of Israel" (*Bamidbar* 1:2). Hashem wanted a precise number. The K'li Yakar explains that this number distinguishes the Jewish people. Things that are numbered are important. Each Jew is very important. So important, that he is guided by *hashgacha pratis* (Hashem's personal supervision). The number expresses that we are important enough to warrant *hashgacha pratis*. The Ramban stresses the same point when he explains the word *"tifkidu"* – you shall count (*Bamidbar* 1:3). This word illustrates that Hashem remembers and supervises. As the verse states, *"VeHashem pakad* (remembered) *es Sarah"* [to grant her a child] (*Bereshis* 21:1). A *pikadon* (from the same root word) is an object that someone watches and supervises for you. This shows that Hashem is watching and supervising each Jew individually.

> *Kinderlach . . .*
>
> *Did you eat a delicious meal today?* Chasdei Hashem *(an act of kindness from Hashem). Did you do well on your test?* Chasdei Hashem. *Did Mommy give you a big, warm, loving hug?* Chasdei Hashem. *Did you bang your toe?* Chasdei Hashem. *Did someone embarrass you?* Chasdei Hashem. *Why are the last two things* Chasdei Hashem? *They are very unpleasant. Because Hashem is personally supervising our lives. Everything that He does is for the good. There are very good reasons for even the unpleasant things. If you hear news about unpleasant things happening, you must know that it is all* Chasdei Hashem. *He is taking care of us, as He has for the past 3800 years.*

Parashas Nasso

No More, No Less

"Mommy, I'm home."

"Chaim, how are you? It is getting late and we were a little worried."

"I'm fine, Mommy. I was having such a good time at the bar mitzvah that I decided to stay a little later."

"Please tell me all about it, Chaim. What is the name of the bar mitzvah boy?"

"Yaakov Hirsch."

"Is he from the Hirsch family that belongs to our shul?"

"Yes Mommy, he is their second son."

"They are a very wealthy family, Chaim. No wonder you stayed a long time at the bar mitzvah. It must have been a very fancy affair. I am sure the food and decorations were very luxurious."

"Not really, Mommy. It was very nice, but nothing out of the ordinary. I stayed long because I was having a great time. Everyone was so warm and friendly. The Hirsch family really is very special. They are so humble that you would never know that they are wealthy."

"I am impressed, Chaim. Here is a family that could have made a very lavish affair, yet they chose to be no different from everyone else. They remind me of Nesanel ben Tsu'ar."

"When was his bar mitzvah?"

"About 3200 years ago."

"Mommy, you're joking."

"No, I am not, Chaim. He was one of the princes of the Tribes of Israel in the desert. He participated in the inauguration of the *Mishkan* (Tabernacle). Betzalel and his artisans built the *Mishkan*. Moshe Rabbeinu assembled it. Aharon HaKohen offered up the first sacrifices. Then came a big inauguration ceremony where each of the princes brought an offering to the *Mishkan*. The first day, Nachshon ben Aminadav, the prince of the tribe of Yehudah brought a beautiful offering consisting of gold, silver, a meal offering, oil, and several animals. Then came the second day. Nesanel ben Tsu'ar, prince of the tribe of Yissachar had his opportunity. He could have brought an even bigger and more elaborate offering. After all, he was a wealthy man, the prince of his tribe. A fancy offering would bring honor to himself and his tribe."

"I can't wait to hear what he brought."

"He brought the exact same offering as Nachshon. Not only that, all of the other princes followed his example and brought the exact same offering."

"Why did they do that, Mommy?"

"Chaim, I will tell you how the Chafetz Chaim explains this event. Nesanel did not want to provoke jealousy among the princes and the tribes. If he brought a nicer offering than Nachshon, then each successive prince would feel obligated to bring an even nicer one. Rivalry and jealousy would arise."

"That was so considerate of him."

"You're right, Chaim. It gave Hashem such pleasure to see His children (the Jewish people) getting along so well that He wrote down each prince's offering separately in the Torah. We all know that the Torah does not waste words. Seventy-two verses are devoted to these wonderful acts of peace and cooperation."

"Mommy, I can think of another benefit of Nesanel's act."

"What is that, Chaim?"

"If they were all trying to outdo each other, then a prince who could not afford a fancier offering would be embarrassed. He might even become poor to buy an offering to keep up with the others. When everyone has the same standard, then no one has to spend lots of money trying to outdo the other."

Kinderlach . . .

Chaim is very perceptive. Just think about how much money is wasted on overly fancy things. Many people become poor because they feel they must keep up with the standard of luxury. The Hirsch family has taught us all a lesson about what is really important at a bar mitzvah. It is not the fancy food, clothing, and decorations. It is the consideration for other people, and the warmth that brings peace. No more, no less. Hashem must have had a lot of pleasure from that bar mitzvah because the Hirsch family kept the same standard as everyone else. No more, no less.

Man's Best Friend

"A man's holy things shall be his, what he gives to the Kohen shall be his" (*Bamidbar* 5:10). If someone gives something away to the Beis Hamikdash or to the Kohen, how can it still be his? The Chafetz Chaim answers this question with a parable from the Midrash.

A man once had three friends. He was very close to the first friend. He was somewhat friendly with the second friend. The third friend received hardly any of his attention. One day this man was called to make an appearance before the king. He was frightened. "What does the king want from me? When the king summons someone it is not a good sign."

The man approached his first friend: "Will you please speak to the king on my behalf? Perhaps the king will look upon me more favorably." The first friend flatly refused. He did not want to have anything to do with the king. Who knows what the king might do to him for defending his friend?

The man went to his second friend. "Will you please speak to the king on my behalf?" The second friend replied, "I will tell you what I will do for you, my friend. I will accompany you to the gates of the palace. After that, you are on your own." The man was crushed. These were his two best friends, whom he had loved and cared for his whole life. What would he do? He had no choice but to go to his third friend, the one whom he hardly paid attention to. He did not hold much hope. His close friends had already refused him. What could he expect from this casual friend?

He said to the third friend, "I am in a tough situation. The king has summoned me and I do not know what to do. Perhaps you can help me out by speaking to the king on my behalf. Put in a good word, a character reference, whatever you can do." He held his breath, waiting for the response. "Do not fear. I will go with you straight to the king, and I will speak on your behalf until you are saved. Nothing will happen to you." And so it was. The third friend went with him to the king and saved him from disaster.

Who is the first friend? That is a man's money. It is very dear to him. He spends much time earning it, investing it, counting it, spending it, and worrying about it. After 120 years, a person faces the King of Kings, Hashem. Can he take his money with him? Not at all. The second friend is a man's family and friends. He spends time with them, although not as much time as he spends at his job. They can give him a funeral procession, a proper sendoff from this world. More than that, they cannot do. Who is that third friend who will speak on his behalf before Hashem? The Torah he learned and the mitzvos he performed. They are the only things that he can take with him to the next world. They will always stand fast at his side.

"A man's holy things shall be his, what he gives to the Kohen shall be his." The holy Torah that he has learned and the holy mitzvos that he has performed—they are his friends forever.

> Kinderlach . . .
> Isn't it wonderful to have a best friend? One who will stick with you through thick and thin. One whom you can count on forever. You can all have a friend like that: learn Torah. Do Hashem's mitzvos. These are the two best friends that a person can have. They will never desert you. They are your friends forever.

Parashas Beha'aloscha

School's Out

"Avi, fancy meeting you here."

"I'm on my way to meet my younger brother at school."

"I am too. We can walk home together."

Ring ring ring ring!
"There's the school bell."

Suddenly, the school doors open and the children burst out, running at full speed.

"Wow, look at that, Chaim. Did you ever see anything like those kids? We had better step out of the way before we are run over."

Chaim slowly shakes his head.

"Three thousand three hundred years."

"These kids haven't been running that long, Chaim. They are not that out of breath."

"I know that, Avi. I meant to say that things have not changed much in 3300 years."

"Sure they have, Chaim. Now we have electricity, telephones, washing machines, and a whole lot of inventions that we did not have 3300 years ago."

"That's true, Avi. But I am taking about human nature."

"Oh, I see. What reminded you of that, Chaim?"

"These kids running out of school. A similar thing happened 3300 years ago."

"Really? What was it?"

"If you look in your *Chumash* at this week's parasha, you will see some funny letters. The letter 'nun' is written upside down and backwards before verse 10:35 and after verse 10:36."

"Let me open my *Chumash* and take a look, Chaim. Wow, look at that. Why is it written that way?"

"Rashi explains that these two verses do not really belong in this place. Hashem moved them from their proper place in the *Chumash* and inserted them here."

"Why?"

"These verses separate two bad events. Before these verses the Torah writes about how the Jewish people traveled quickly from Har Sinai after the giving of the Torah, like a child running from school. Just as a child feels that he has learned enough for the day, so too they felt that they had learned a lot of Torah. They were afraid that if they stayed longer, Hashem might give them more mitzvos."

"Afraid? Mitzvos are great! We should run towards them, not away from them."

"So true, Avi."

"I have a story for you about how great mitzvos are, Chaim. Do you want to hear it?"

"Sure, Avi."

"There once was a man who landed a job polishing gems. He was to be paid for each stone that he polished. The first day of work, he received five stones to polish. He happily finished his work and got paid for the day. He noticed that the worker next to him received twenty stones that day. The next day he reported for work and again received five stones to polish. He finished the job quickly and watched his neighbor working hard, polishing twenty stones. He was a little upset but figured that since he was new at the job, he did not yet receive a full workload. However, the situation did not change. Every day he received five stones, while his neighbor received twenty. One day he could no longer hold back. He went to the boss complaining, 'What are you doing? Why aren't you giving me more work? I came here to work and make money! Give me work so that I can make money!'"

"That's a great story, Avi."

"It is a parable to the mitzvos and their reward. The gems are like mitzvos and the pay is like the reward that we receive for doing the mitzvos. So you see, Chaim, mitzvos may be hard work, but they give us great reward. We came to this world to work at doing the mitzvos to earn the reward. The Mishnah in *Makkos* (3:16) relates that Rebbe Chanania ben Akashia taught: Hashem wanted to reward the Jewish people. That is why He gave them such a large Torah and so many mitzvos. As the Prophet (*Yeshaya* 42:21) says, 'Hashem wants the Jews to be tzaddikim, therefore he enlarged and strengthened the Torah.'"

"As we were talking, Avi, our little brothers have come out of school."

"Come, boys. Let's walk home. We have a story for you."

"Great! We're so out of breath after running so hard."

"Well, I have news for you. After you hear this story, you will want to run back to school faster than you ran out of school."

"What? Run back to school? School's out!"

"That's what you think."

Kinderlach . . .
Each mitzvah is a gem. Each word of Torah that you learn is a diamond. Wealth and good fortune are yours. Free for the taking. Learn Torah and do the mitzvos. School is the place to learn how to learn. In school you are learning a profession that will make you very wealthy. If they were giving out ice cream, you would run to be the first one in line. At school they are giving something much better. Run to school and get your prize.

Always At Home

"All aboard, train #545, leaving in five minutes on track #3! All aboard!"

A mother stood with her infant baby, waiting for her husband to arrive on the next train. The noise of the busy train station frightened the baby.

"Waaaaa! Waaaaa! Waaaaa!"
"Sha, baby. Sha, sha, sha."

The mother lifted the baby out of her stroller and hugged her in her arms.

"Sha, baby. Sha, sha, sha."

The baby quickly quieted down, comforted by her mother's embrace.

"Upon Hashem's word they camped, and upon Hashem's word they traveled" (*Bamidbar* 9:20). Rav Chaim Shmuelevitz explains that a baby's home is in the mother's arms. The baby can travel to the ends of the world, yet if he is in his mother's arms, he is always home. The *Lekach Tov* explains that the

Jewish people trusted Hashem. They followed Him into the desert, into an unsown land (*Yirmiyahu* 2:2). Their trust was so complete that wherever they traveled, they always saw themselves in His presence—like a baby always feels at home in its mother's arms.

> *Kinderlach . . .*
> *Don't you enjoy coming home? It is cold and rainy outside, and the wind is howling. You open the door to the house and step inside the warm room. Mommy's warm smile and the smell of delicious chicken soup on the fire are there to greet you. It's great to be home.*
> *We are always at home. Hashem is our home. Wherever we are, He is with us and we are with Him. When you feel lonely, open your Tehillim (Psalms) and call to Him. He will warm your heart. It's great to be home.*

Parashas Shelach

The Outsider

"Quickly! Close the door!"

The children had never seen their father so frantic. He rushed in the house, panting and out of breath. He slammed the door behind him and double-locked it.

"What is the matter, Daddy?"

"Someone is trying to get in here. Do not open this door under any circumstances."

There was a light knock at the door. The children crowded around the peephole. Outside was a very sweet looking elderly man, smiling warmly.

"Daddy. A nice old man is outside. Maybe he needs a drink. Can we open the door for him?"

"No way! That old man may look nice, but he is nothing but trouble. He will smile sweetly and just ask you to open the door. He won't even want to come in. He will just ask to stand outside and talk for a few minutes. Then he will say that he is embarrassed talking in the hallway. He will want to come just inside the door. Then he will ask if he can sit on a stool beside the door.

"Next he will want to sit on the couch. He will soon be telling Mommy how to serve the meals, and telling the girls how to dress. He will give me all kinds of reasons to be late for my learning session. In short, he will take over the whole house and our lives. He will cause all kinds of arguments, hatred, and bitterness, in addition to many other sins."

"Abba, I don't believe it. Who is this man? He looks so innocent and sweet."

"His name is *Yetzer Hara*. He looks like a softie, but he is strong as iron. The only way to defeat him is to keep him outside the door. Do not let him in, even for an instant."

Kinderlach . . .
The yetzer hara is always trying to push his way inside. He convinced the spies to say lashon hara about the Land of Israel. He is very subtle. "Just do a little sin. It won't hurt you. Just do it once and get it out of your system." This is one of his favorite tricks. He only wants to come in for a minute. Then he promises not to bother you anymore. There is only one way to beat him. Make him the outsider. Keep the yetzer hatov inside, and slam the door on the yetzer hara.

Ladders to Heaven

"Mommy, I'm home."

"Chaim, it's so good to see your smiling face. How was school?"

"Great."

"Come, have some lunch now."

"Thanks, Mommy. I hope you don't mind but I would like to eat quickly because I have a lot of studying to do."

"Do you have a test tomorrow, Chaim?"

"Yes I do, Mommy. It covers a lot of material so I have to study very hard."

"Chaim, you give me so much *nachas*; you make me so proud. You are such a dedicated student. I am very proud of you."

"Thanks, Mommy. I have to go now."

With that, Chaim hurries to his room to begin studying.
One hour later, his mother softly knocks on the door.

"Chaim, may I come in?"

"Sure, Mommy."

"I brought you some cookies and milk. How is your studying going?"

"No so good, Mommy. There is so much to learn. How will I ever have the time to finish?"

"Don't get discouraged, Chaim. Rav Yisrael Salanter was the great Rav who founded the *Mussar* movement. It stresses working on perfecting one's self. He used to say that there is

no sickness worse than despair."

"I am feeling discouraged, Mommy. Can you help me?"

"Let me tell you a story about another time in history when the entire Jewish people were feeling discouraged. It was the time of the *Meraglim* (spies)."

"I know that story, Mommy. The Jewish people were about to enter the Land of Israel. They sent spies to check out the Land first."

"Very good, Chaim! What did the spies find?"

"Ten of them brought back a bad report about the land. It would be too difficult to conquer."

"Excellent, Chaim. The people became very discouraged when they heard this. Two spies, Calev and Yehoshua, saw the good in the Land. Calev tried to encourage the people: 'Go up and inherit the land because you are surely able to.' Rashi comments that he was telling them that they would be able to build ladders and go up to heaven, if need be. Success was theirs."

"Really, Mommy? Ladders to heaven? Ladders do not reach to heaven. If they were able to reach heaven, it would be a miracle. If Hashem performed a miracle for them, they would not need ladders."

"Chaim, you are really on the ball today. You have asked the same question that the great Rav Moshe Feinstein asked."

"What's the answer?"

"The Torah is teaching us that we must show Hashem how much we want something. Of course, it is impossible to climb up a ladder to heaven. But that does not mean that we do not have to try. Hashem can make the impossible happen. He can work miracles. But He will only do that for us if we show Him how much we want the miracle to happen."

"How do we show Him?"

"By trying our hardest. Rav Moshe Feinstein writes about Torah learning as an example. Hashem gave us a whole big Torah to learn. How can we ever hope to know it all?"

"That is how I feel about my test, Mommy."

"Rav Moshe is speaking to you, Avi. Show Hashem how much you want to learn and know the Torah. He will then give you a nice big present."

"Really?"

"Yes. You will learn and know much more Torah than you ever thought possible. All you have to do is try. Some of our greatest rabbis were not the smartest boys in the class. But they were the hardest workers."

"Mommy, you have really helped me. I'm not giving up. I'm going to try my hardest and study my best for this test."

"Avi, your ladders are already reaching up to heaven."

Kinderlach . . .

Don't ever despair. And don't ever give up. Hashem never gives anyone a job that he cannot handle. Does your job seem difficult? Perhaps you can try again. A little harder this time. And turn to Hashem for help. He wants you to realize that He is the One Who is giving you the test. He can help you. Start climbing those ladders to heaven.

Parashas Korach

It Always Spells Trouble

"Mommy, can you help me with my spelling?"

"Sure, Chaim. Hebrew spelling or English?"

"Hebrew. How do you spell *machlokes*?"

"That's easy. *Mem, ches, lamed, kuf, taf.* Do you want to hear something about the word *machlokes*, Chaim?"

"Sure, Mommy."

"It always spells trouble."

"What do you mean, Mommy? I thought *machlokes* means argument."

"You are correct, Chaim. The word *machlokes* does mean dispute. This week's parasha describes the first *machlokes* in Jewish history. Korach challenged Moshe Rabbeinu."

"That's terrible."

"You're not kidding, Chaim. Let me tell you just how terrible it was. The Midrash Rabba relates five points, one for each letter of the word *machlokes*, that show how terrible a senseless dispute really is. 'Mem' is for *makkah* (a beating). 'Ches' is for *charon* (wrath). 'Lamed' is for *likui* (stricken).

'*Kuf*' is for *k'lalah* (a curse). '*Taf*' is for *to'eivah* (abomination). Argument brings beating, anger, strikes, curse, and abomination upon a person."

"Oy vey."

"Chaim, let us use our imagination for a minute. Imagine that you were about to go to a new school. The teachers seemed nice. The building was nice. The students seemed friendly. You asked a few more questions and found out that terrible things were happening in that school. There were beatings, sickness, and curses. Terrible sins were being committed. Would you go to that school?"

"Of course not, Mommy. I would stay as far away from it as possible."

"Chaim, We must stay as far away from *machlokes* as we would from that school. Let me tell you something else about the spelling of the word *machlokes*, Chaim. The *Maharzav* commentary on the Midrash Rabba spells the word *machlokes* backward, with a word for each letter. '*Tachlis kilyon l'olam chalukah meivi*' (Argument's purpose is to bring destruction to the world)."

"Mommy, I never realized how terrible an argument really is. Can you give me some pointers on how to avoid *machlokes*?"

"Chaim dear, when you find yourself disagreeing with someone you must ask yourself, 'Is this argument really worth it? What are we really arguing about anyway? Is it that important?' Even if it is important, is there another way to settle it besides arguing?'"

"That is really great advice, Mommy. But sometimes, I just know the other side is wrong."

"That does not always matter, Chaim. You might think that you will win the argument. But there is only one winner in an argument. The *yetzer hara* (evil inclination). Everyone else loses."

> *Kinderlach . . .*
>
> *Now you see how terrible an argument really is. You might think that you will win the argument. Even if you 'win,' you almost always lose. Bad feelings are aroused which cause resentment. Close relationships are damaged. It's just not worth it. The best way to win an argument is to avoid it. Win every argument—avoid them all. Do you know what that spells? Success.*

It's Not My Job

"Mommy, where is the phone book?"

"Over there in the cabinet, Avi. Maybe I can help you. Whose phone number do you need?"

"I want to call a boy in my class. He cheated by looking at my paper during the test today. I am so upset. He deserves a punishment. I am really going to tell him what I think about him. That will teach him a lesson."

"Let us think about this a minute before you call him, Avi. Are you sure that he cheated?

"One hundred percent, Mommy. I saw him looking at my paper and writing down my answers."

"I see. The first thing that you should try to do is to correct his mistake. I suggest that you wait until you are a little calmer. Then you can call him and explain to him that he was wrong."

"Mommy, I don't want to correct his mistake. I just want to teach him a lesson."

"Hmmm. Avi, you know that the Torah forbids that. We are not allowed to take revenge."

"But Mommy, I'm so upset."

"I understand, Avi dear. Let me tell you what happened to me yesterday. I hired a woman to help with the housecleaning. We agreed that she would do the dishes, the laundry, vacuum the carpets, and mop the floors. She came and did a very good job. Then I asked her to do the windows. Do you know what she said?"

"It's not my job."

"Right. I was a little upset. However, she was 100% right. She never agreed to do windows. She knew very clearly what jobs were hers and what jobs were not."

"That is very nice, Mommy, but what does it have to do with cheating on the test?"

"Avi, in this week's parasha, Korach rebelled against Moshe Rabbeinu. He made false accusations. He started an unjustified argument. He mocked Moshe Rabbeinu. He refused any attempts to make peace. He turned many people against their beloved leader."

"Those are all pretty terrible things, Mommy. He really deserved punishment for them."

"He certainly did, Avi, and he got it."

"Who gave it to him? Moshe Rabbeinu?"

"Not at all, Avi. Moshe Rabbeinu tried to make peace with him. Moshe went to Korach privately, in order to avoid embarrassing him. Moshe answered all of Korach's accusations and patiently explained the reasons for his actions. However, all of his attempts failed."

"What happened next, Mommy? Did Moshe punish him?"

"No, Avi. That was not his job. That was Hashem's job. Moshe Rabbeinu's job was to try to make peace with Korach. He tried to correct Korach's mistakes and set him on the straight path. He tried to help Korach in every possible way. However, nothing succeeded. There was no choice but to punish him."

"Right, Mommy. Some people deserve punishment."

"Yes, Avi. However, that is not our job. It is Hashem's job. He delivers the reward and punishment. Hashem punished Korach and all of his followers."

"Mommy, what you are saying is that I should not try to teach this boy a lesson. It is not my job."

"Exactly, Avi."

"Mommy, sometimes you and Daddy punish me. You say that you are only doing it to teach me a lesson. What is the difference?"

"We are your parents, Avi. We have a mitzvah to educate you properly. Sometimes, punishment is a necessary part of education. Teachers are also trying to help you when they punish you. That is their job."

"But it is so unfair, Mommy! How can he get away with that? How can that boy cheat and not pay for it?"

"Avi, nothing is unfair. Hashem is running the world. No one gets away with anything. We all have faith in Hashem. He does not allow any wrong deed to go unpunished. Punishment is His job."

Kinderlach . . .

Do your job, and leave Hashem to do His job. This rule will bring you much happiness and peace of mind. You will never get upset like Avi did. You will never try to do Hashem's job. Concentrate on doing your job as well as you can. Whenever you feel yourself wanting to take revenge or teach the other person a lesson, say these simple words to yourself: "It's not my job."

Parashas Chukas

I Want To Speak To The Boss

"Young man, may I help you?"

"Yes sir, I would like to speak to the boss, if I may."

"Is there something that I can help you with?"

Thank you for your offer, but no. It is a private matter which is very important."

"Very well, young man. The office of the store manager is in the back. I will take you there."

The boy knocks softly on the door. A voice on the other side replies.

"Yes, come in please."

"Excuse me, Mr. Manager. I'm very sorry to disturb you. I have a very important matter to discuss with the boss."

"I'll be frank with you, young man. I am just the manager of this store. It is one of several chain stores in this city. The main office is downtown. You will find the boss there."

"I see, sir. Okay. I will go downtown. Thank you for your time."

"My pleasure, young man."

The boy gets the address of the main office and the bus directions from the salesman. He gets on the bus, and in no time arrives downtown at the main office.

"Yes, young man, may I help you?" asks the receptionist.

"Yes ma'am. I would like to speak to the boss of all the chain stores."

The receptionist is a little surprised by the request.

"Young man, the boss is a very busy man. He has meetings and appointments all day. People do not usually walk in to speak to him without prior arrangements."

"I'm sorry. I did not realize that. However, this is an important matter."

The receptionist senses the boy's sincerity.

"Just a minute. Perhaps I can squeeze you in between appointments."

She calls the boss's secretary, explaining the unusual request.

"Yes? Ten minutes? Thank you very much. Young man, you may go in to see the boss in ten minutes. Just take that elevator up to the twenty seventh floor."

"Thank you very much, ma'am."

The boy takes the elevator and finds the boss's secretary. In exactly ten minutes, he is ushered in to the office. He sees the boss sitting behind a huge wooden desk.

"Yes, young man. How can I help you?"

"Thank you for seeing me sir. I have an important

monetary matter to discuss with you. It concerns some neighbors of mine."

"Go ahead young man."

"There is a poor family on my street. They do not have enough money to buy all of the food that they need. One of your stores is right on the corner. Perhaps the store could provide them with two loaves of bread and two liters of milk every day?"

The CEO's heart is warmed by the boy's sincerity. He smiles warmly, strokes his beard, and adjusts his kippa.

"The truth is, young man, the company does not give me the authority to grant such a request. Our chain of stores is owned by an international conglomerate. The main office is overseas."

The boy's face fell.

"Sir, why is it so difficult to speak to the boss?"

"Young man, I am going to grant you your request myself. Here is my own personal check with enough money for bread, milk, chicken and vegetables for a month. Just give me your address, and I will mail a check every month to take care of this family. There is just one condition."

"What is that sir?"

"You must come with me now on a short trip."

"Okay."

The CEO puts on his hat and jacket and heads for the elevator. All of the employees greet him as he exits the building with the young boy. They walk to the end of the block, make a left turn, and come to a Beit Kinesset. The boss opens the door, and they walk inside.

"Young man, you asked me why it is so difficult to speak to the boss. It is really not difficult at all. The True Boss is the Almighty King of Kings. We are all just His servants and messengers here on earth. Whenever you have a request, speak to Him directly. He is always happy to hear from you."

"You are very clever, sir."

"Hashem heard the voice of Israel . . ." (Bamidbar 21:3). The Jewish people had prayed to Hashem asking for a victory over the Canaanite king of Arad. He answered their prayers, delivering the enemy into their hands. Hashem wants our prayers. He wants us to turn to Him with all of our requests. He is the Ultimate Boss of the universe. He has many ways to grant our requests. We just need to sincerely ask.

Kinderlach . . .

We pray three times a day. It is easy to fall into a bad habit and forget that we are speaking to Hashem. The Mishna (Pirkei Avot 2:13) warns against this. "Rebbe Shimon says, 'Be careful when you recite Kriyat Shema and pray. Do not allow your prayers to become routine, but appeal for mercy and favor before Hashem.'" Kinderlach, remember to Whom you are speaking. As you take three steps forward before you begin the Amida, imaging that you are walking down a corridor through a doorway. On the other side is the Shechina *(Divine Presence). Your prayers will be completely different. May Hashem fulfill all of your wishes for the good.*

The Value of Shalom

"What a beautiful gem! What is it?"
"A diamond."
"Look at how it sparkles. It must be very valuable."
"It is quite expensive."
"The ring that it is set in is also nice. I have a silly question for you. If you needed the ring for something else, would you throw away the diamond to use the ring?"
"Of course not. The diamond is much more valuable than the ring."

This week's parasha relates the death of Aharon HaKohen (*Bamidbar* 20:27–29). The entire Jewish people, both men and women, mourned him—because he loved peace and pursued it.

People sometimes get confused. They have a good relationship with a friend or a neighbor. Then they get into a disagreement about money, or building repairs, or a seat in shul. What do they do? They allow the disagreement to ruin the relationship and they bear a grudge against the person. Good relationships between people are as valuable as diamonds. They are the *shalom* in the world that Hashem wants so much. Throwing away a good relationship over a money dispute is like throwing away the diamond and saving the ring.

> *Kinderlach . . .*
>
> *Don't get confused. Let Aharon HaKohen be your guide. Always make good relationships your main goal. Always try to be nice and giving to people in order to develop good relationships. When you get into disagreements, do not let them ruin the relationship. Usually the disagreement is over something that is worth far less than the relationship. Save the relationship and keep the diamond for yourself.*

Parashas Balak

Obsession

"*Aleinu, ve'al kol amo Yisrael vi'imru amen.*"

"Amen."

"Good Shabbos, Avi."

"Good Shabbos, Daddy."

"Now that the morning prayers are over, would you like to stay here in the shul for the Kiddush?"

"Sure, Daddy. What's the occasion?"

"The bar mitzvah of our neighbor, Zevi."

"Great, they're setting up the tables now. Let's help them bring out the food."

"You are a real tzaddik, Avi."

The tablecloths are spread, and the cakes brought out. Drinks, fruit, and snack treats are added to the cuisine. As the last food reaches the tables, the adults begin to sit down for Kiddush. Suddenly, one energetic young boy runs close to the table, pushes through the crowd, steps on three men's shoes, and jumps over the back of the bench. He lands in a seat in front of the cake, shoving away a man who was sitting there. The crowd of people is appalled at the behavior of this young boy.

"Avi, it is ironic that something like this should happen this week."

"Why, Daddy? What is so special about this week?"

"This morning we read Parashas Balak."

"I don't recall any mention of jumping over benches in the parasha."

"Of course not, Avi. But let me tell you about Bilaam. Although he was not a Jew, he was a prophet. In addition to that, he had an amazing power to bless and curse people."

"Anyone can bless and curse people, Daddy."

"Yes, Avi, but his blessings and curses came true."

"Amazing."

"Balak, king of Moav, heard about the military victories of the Jewish people on their way to the Land of Israel. He feared for his life and the lives of his people."

"What did he do? Train more soldiers?"

"No, Avi. He sought out Bilaam, whose curses were more powerful than any army or weapon. He sent prestigious messengers, who requested that Bilaam come. But Bilaam wanted more honor. Balak sent higher-ranking officials. But Bilaam wanted silver and gold."

"What happened?"

"Bilaam was promised everything he wanted, and asked Hashem if he could go to do the job for Balak. Hashem granted him permission. Bilaam could not wait to get the money. He got up early the next morning, saddled up his faithful donkey, and went with the officers of Moav. Hashem was not going to make this easy for him. He sent an angel down from heaven, which stood in front of the donkey.

"Bilaam could not see the angel, but the donkey saw it. The donkey turned aside. Bilaam was so upset with the delay that he hit the donkey with his staff. The donkey started moving, only to encounter the angel again. The donkey stopped and Bilaam again hit it. Finally the donkey was in a narrow place, and the angel stood directly in front of it. It had no place to move, so it stopped. Bilaam's anger burned and he smashed it with his staff."

"I know what happened next, Daddy. Hashem opened the mouth of the donkey and it spoke to Bilaam."
"Very good, Avi. What did Bilaam do after that?"
"He answered back to the donkey: 'You mocked me. If I had a sword in my hand, I would kill you.' That is unbelievable, Daddy."
"I know, Avi. I am amazed every time I read that verse. Could you imagine experiencing such a miracle? A donkey talking? I would be flabbergasted. I would be in such shock that I would not be able to speak."
"How could Bilaam talk, Daddy?"
"That is the point of the story, Avi. He was so caught up in running after money and honor that he was furious with anyone who tried to stop him. He only saw the donkey as an obstacle. The fact that it spoke was irrelevant to him."
"Wow. It is amazing that a person can be so caught up in his desires."

"Exactly, Avi. We all must be careful. It can happen to any one of us. That young boy smelled the fresh cake, and would not let anything or anyone stand in his way. Even if it meant pushing, jumping, and shoving. He was obsessed."

"This has taught me a real lesson, Daddy."

"What, Avi?"

"To be obsessed."

"Avi!"

"With doing mitzvos, helping people, and learning Torah."

"Avi, I am obsessed with you. You are a wonderful son."

"Thank you, Daddy."

Kinderlach . . .

Don't be obsessed with treats and toys. Always keep a cool head. Keep things in perspective. Is it so terrible if you do not get the biggest piece of cake? It is more important to behave properly. Everyone wants to be first in line, but not at the expense of pushing others out of the way. Be obsessed with being a mensch.

Dignity

"Avi, fancy meeting you here. I thought that I was the only one who knew this shortcut home from school."

"Not at all, Chaim. I have been going this way for a long time. I like walking past these new homes. Look at that one, the front door is wide open. Wow, you can see straight into the house. Hmmm. That is really interesting. It looks like they are doing some remodeling in there."

"Avi, should you be looking into someone's front door?"

"Well, they left it wide open. They must know that people will look in."

"I see that they have left it open. However, I still do not think that we should look in. After all, looking into someone's home is an invasion of privacy. People do things inside of their homes that they do not want others to see."

"I guess you're right, Chaim. But why do they build their home in such a way that you can see right into the front door from the street?"

"That's a good question, Avi. The homes should be built to provide more privacy. Just as it was in the desert."

"The desert? Who had a private home in the desert?"

"The Jewish people's homes were very private during their wanderings in the desert over three thousand years ago."

"Didn't they live in tents?"

"They surely did."

"Tents are not very private."

"Usually not, Avi. However, they were very careful to pitch their tents in such a way that no two openings faced each other."

"That is not so easy to do. How do you know that, Chaim?"

"It is in this week's parasha, Avi. The wicked Bilaam wanted to curse the Jewish people. Hashem would not allow him to curse us. He only let him bless us. Bilaam went to the top of a mountain and looked down on the Jewish encampment. He said, 'How good are your tents, Yaakov, your dwellings, Israel' (*Bamidbar* 24:5). Rashi comments that Bilaam saw that the openings of their tents were not facing each other. This was a true blessing, complimenting the *tznius* (modesty and dignity) of the Jewish people. They respected each other's privacy. They would not look into each other's homes."

"I see what you mean, Chaim. Looking into someone's house is really prying into their business. We have no right to do that. It shows a lack of self-respect and respect for the other person."

"Exactly, Avi."

Kinderlach . . .

One of the trademarks of the Jewish people has always been our tznius. *We express it in many ways. Our clothing, manners of speech, even the way we walk, all reflect our modesty and dignity. Be proud to be a member of this people. We have maintained our dignity through the many struggles of our three thousand years of history. Make your effort to carry on the tradition. Do not look into people's homes. Think two or three times before asking them a personal question. Dress, walk, and talk with dignity. Uphold the nobility of the Jewish people.*

Parashas Pinchas

No Strain, No Gain

"Take a deep breath. Breathe out. Another one. Breathe out."

"What do you hear in my breathing, doctor?"

"Mr. Weiss, perhaps you should take a deep breath and relax before I begin to speak."

"Oh no."

"Here are the facts. You have high blood pressure. You also have high cholesterol. You are 40 pounds overweight and you smoke cigarettes. You are a high risk candidate for heart disease, Heaven forbid."

"I was afraid of this. What can I do, doctor?"

"In short, Mr. Weiss, you should give up smoking, go on a low-fat diet of no more than 1200 calories per day, and exercise at least 20 minutes per day."

"Doctor, what you are prescribing sounds hard."

"I know, Mr. Weiss. It *is* very difficult. I went through the same thing myself, a few years ago."

"Really, doctor? You are so thin."

"It was hard work. When I began the diet, I was hungry

most of the time."

"How did you overcome that feeling?"

"I kept repeating one thing over and over to myself. This feeling of hunger tells me that I am losing weight. That is bringing me closer to good health. As my weight went down, I began to feel better and better. I actually welcomed and enjoyed that hungry feeling because I knew that it was improving my health and making me feel good. The same thing was true with the exercise."

"Amazing, doctor."

"As they say in athletics, 'no strain, no gain.'"

"We say that in the Torah, also."

"Really? I don't recall having learned that in my parashas hashavuah class."

"Did you learn about the *korbanos* (sacrifices), doctor?"

"Yes. The various sacrifices brought on the Holy Days are mentioned in Parashas Pinchas."

"Right. You use the word 'sacrifice' when referring to a *korban*, doctor."

"Isn't that the translation?"

"Not precisely. The word *korban* comes from the word *karov*, to come closer. A *korban* brings a person closer to Hashem."

"That is a wonderful idea."

"The word 'sacrifice' is rooted in the idea that you gave up your money to buy a *korban*."

"That is not so unusual, people spend money on many

things."

"Yes, but this animal was burned on the Altar. The owner got no physical benefit from it."

"That was a real sacrifice."

"In a manner of speaking. However, by giving up that money, he came closer to Hashem. That is something which has more value than all of the money in the world."

"I see. I think I understand your point, Mr. Weiss. By giving up something, you become closer to your goal."

"Exactly. That is how you described your diet and exercise program to me. You don't mind giving up the excess food because it is bringing you closer to good health."

"Mr. Weiss, that is wonderful. I am sure that this insight will motivate you to do well on your health program."

"I'm ready for the strain, doctor."

"The gain is all yours, Mr. Weiss."

Kinderlach . . .

Anything worthwhile in life requires sacrifice. Success in learning, mitzvos, and good middos (character traits) all require a sacrifice of time and effort. However, it is time well spent. People spend lots of time earning money. They put their full efforts into it. As the verse states, "If you seek it like silver, and search for it like hidden treasures, then you will understand the fear of Hashem and discover the knowledge of Hashem" (Mishlei 2:4-5). Put your time and effort into Torah. The strain is all gain.

The Reward

"Chaim, can I help you with your load?"

"Sure, Avi."

"What are you carrying here?"

"Well, I have a shofar and a lulav in this bag. I have some matza and tefillin in the other bag. Now, in this hand I have tzitzis and some wine for Kiddush. I have a Megillah behind my back, and a *bris mila* knife in my pocket, along with some money to give to tsedaka."

"Wow! Where are you going with all of these things, and what are you going to do when you get there?"

"I am going to the yeshiva to learn Torah."

"Pardon me for asking, but you have a lot of mitzvah items with you. Why do you need to take them with you when you learn Torah?"

"I don't really need them to learn, Avi. They are just a reminder."

"Now you really have my curiosity going. What do all of these things remind you of?"

"That the reward for learning Torah is equal to all of the other mitzvos combined."

"I see. You are very clever, Chaim."

"I just don't want to forget the importance of learning Torah."

The parasha speaks about a census taken of the Jewish people, tribe by tribe, after the sin of Baal Peor. The fifth tribe

counted was Yissachar. The Ohr HaChaim HaKadosh relates that the name "Yissachar" is a combination of the words *"yesh s'char"* (there is a reward). The *gematria* (numerical equivalent) of *"yesh"* is 310. The members of the tribe of Yissachar were all very learned in Torah. Their reward is stated in the very last Mishnah of the Talmud (*Uktzin* 3:12): "In the future, Hashem will maintain 310 worlds for each tzaddik." The Bartenura explains that the tzaddik receives this reward because he learned and kept all of the *Mishnayos*. That is the great reward for learning Torah.

Kinderlach . . .
Every mitzvah has a wonderful reward. However, one mitzvah outweighs all of the others: learning Torah. Try to imagine putting on tefillin, making Kiddush, eating matza, sitting in the sukkah, giving tsedaka, saying Shema, and doing all of the other mitzvos in the Torah at the same time. What a reward! With each word of Torah that you learn, you receive that reward. Mind boggling. 310 worlds await you. How can you even think of wasting one minute?

Parashas Mattos

Forget About Anger

"Hello. Yes. How are you? I wanted to ask you what's doing with our little project? What??? You did what??? I can't believe it. That is terrible. I cannot talk any longer. I'm too upset. I'm sorry. I'll have to call you back later. Good bye."

"Who was that, Daddy?"

"Someone I was doing business with, Chaim."

"Are you finished now, Daddy?"

"Yes, Chaim."

"Can we learn Torah, now?"

"Sure, Chaim."

"You said that you had something special that you wanted to learn with me, Daddy."

"I remember saying that, Chaim. But I can't remember what I wanted to learn."

"Really, Daddy? You have such a great memory."

"Thank you, Chaim. I just can't seem to remember that Torah subject."

"Can I tell you something that I learned today, Daddy?"

"With pleasure, Chaim."

"We learned that when a person gets upset, he forgets his Torah learning."

"How appropriate, Chaim. Where did you learn that?"

"In our parashas hashavuah class. Moshe Rabbeinu became angry with the Jewish people."

"Why, Chaim?"

"Hashem gave them very specific instructions on how to fight the war against the nation of Midian. Moshe, Elazar, and the princes went out to meet the soldiers when they returned from the war. They did not follow Moshe's instructions, and he became angry."

"What did he forget?"

"The people wanted to know the laws of kashering the cooking vessels that they had taken from the Midianities. Elazar the Kohen Gadol had to teach these laws, because Moshe had forgotten them. Rashi inform us that this is one of the three places in the Torah where Moshe became angry."

"I see, Chaim. I am not the only one who forgot my learning because I became angry."

"Not at all, Daddy."

"Chaim, a great Jewish sage who lived about 800 years ago named Rabbi Moses ben Nachman, known to us as the Ramban, wrote a famous letter about anger. This letter explains how anger is a terrible character trait, which can drag a person down to the lowest levels."

"Oy vey."

"The problem is that our *yetzer hara* makes us think that

anger is good. If we lose our temper, everything will be okay. We will let off steam, and the other person will see how terribly he behaved. Things will calm down afterward, and we will have gotten our way. People will appreciate how upset we were and will empathize with us."

"What a fantasy."

"Exactly, Chaim. The *yetzer hara* is a master at taking something that is truly terrible, and wrapping it up in a beautiful package. Imagine receiving a beautifully gift-wrapped box. You can't wait to open it up. You finally get to the inside and find . . ."

"A poisonous snake."

"Exactly, Chaim. That is what the *yetzer hara* does."

"What can we do to stop him?"

Kinderlach . . .

The Ramban advises that a person should develop the habit of speaking softly to everyone at all times. Then he will be saved from the awful trait of anger and all the damage it does. Wouldn't it be wonderful if we never raised our voice, and never got angry? It is within our power. When we recognize that feeling of anger rising within us, let us lower the tone of our voice, or not say anything altogether. This will prevent us from getting angry. Kinderlach, forget about anger, and remember every piece of Torah that you learn.

Know Your Enemy

"Take vengeance for the Children of Israel against Midian" (*Bamidbar* 31:2). Vengeance? How can it be? The Torah forbids taking revenge (*Vayikra* 19:18). How can Hashem command Moshe to violate a mitzvah of the Torah? Rav Shimshon Refael Hirsch explains that the war against Midian was a different type of retribution. Hashem's Torah rests upon two foundations: *tznius* (modesty) and *emunah* (faith in Hashem). The nation of Midian tried to undermine both of these.

When going to war, one must know who his enemy is. Midian was not the usual adversary, who tries to kill his foe and destroy him physically. Rather, this enemy tried to bring spiritual death upon us. They made us stumble and commit the worst sins. They tried to ruin our souls. That is true destruction.

Therefore, we went to war. Hashem commanded Moshe Rabbeinu to take revenge. This was not a personal grudge, nor a national grudge. Rather, this was a war fought to strengthen the Jewish people spiritually. We stand spiritually strong when the enemies of the soul, and everything that they stand for, are destroyed.

Kinderlach . . .

We are still fighting against the enemy who tries to undermine modesty in Klal Yisrael. "Mommy, can you buy that dress for me?" "Let's try it on, Shiffy. Hmmm. It's a bit too short and tight." "Really, Mommy? Everyone wears dresses like this. It's the latest style." "Shiffy, do you know who sets the trends for the latest styles?" "No, Mommy. Please tell me." "Fashion designers and promoters in far-away lands. They have no knowledge of our Holy Torah and its concept of tznius. Their only concern is to sell clothes. We have different interests: to guard the holiness of our souls, which come down to this earth from under Hashem's Holy Throne. Fashion styles come and go, but the Jewish soul is eternal. Would anyone want to exchange eternity for a piece of cloth?" "Mommy, you are always so inspiring." "Shiffy, our modern world is full of challenges to test our faith in Hashem. Technology can be a friend or an enemy. It can accomplish wondrous things. However, it is so powerful that it can totally distract us from serving Hashem properly. We have to fight a war against the enemies of our soul." "I'm with you, Mommy. We will defeat the enemy."

Parashas Masei

It Takes Time

"Doctor Kalter, I can't take it anymore."

"What is the problem Mr. Hayes?"

"This hot weather. Every day is summer. 365 days a year. Hot and humid. I can no longer live here in the tropics. I want to move to the North Pole."

"That's quite an extreme change, My Hayes. Do you realize that at the North Pole it is freezing cold winter 365 days a year?"

"I don't care. It will be a pleasure after this heat."

"You may feel like that for the first few hours or even the first day or two. However, after that you will become very cold and uncomfortable. You body cannot take such an extreme change in such a short time."

"But I want to live there Doctor Kalter."

"Then you have to make a gradual change Mr. Hayes. Move a little farther north, where the weather is a little cooler. When you become accustomed to that weather, make another move farther north. You will become accustomed to the cooler weather over there also. Keep moving farther and farther north, slowly, and deliberately. Eventually, you will reach the North Pole. By then you will be accustomed to the climate."

"What you are saying, Dr. Kalter, is that a drastic change must be made patiently, and in slow steps."

"Precisely."

"These are the journeys of the Children of Israel" (Bamidbar 33:1). The Malbim asks, "Why did the Children of Israel need to wait forty years before entering the Land of Israel? Hashem could have brought them in immediately." The answer is that they were not ready. They had sunken into the lowest level of impurity in Mitzraim. They could not pull out of it immediately, as their many mistakes in the *midbar* proved. And so, they needed time. To slowly but surely purify themselves. Only then, would they be ready to enter the Holy Land.

Kinderlach . . .

Some things happen quickly. Others take time. Working on improving ones character traits takes time. It is a long-term project that lasts a lifetime. For this, we need patience. Changes do not happen overnight. Progress is made, but there are also setbacks. Two steps forward, one step back. Listen to the words of the verse, "For though the tzaddik may fall seven times, he will arise" (Mishlei 24:16). Have patience with yourselves, kinderlach. Become tzaddikim.

Selfish Flattery

"Here comes the head of the department," Mr. Cohen thought to himself. "I can strike up a conversation with him. Then he can see how capable I am. That will increase my chances for a promotion."

"How are you, Mr. Jones? How are things going in the marketing department?"

"Not so well, Mr. Cohen. We have a lot of 'dead weight' around here. Mr. Schwartz who works in public relations comes late every day, takes long breaks, and goes home early."

"Oh no," thought Mr. Cohen. "He is speaking lashon hora. What shall I do? Perhaps I should just walk away. Maybe I will put my fingers in my ears. Better yet, I should tell him to stop. How can I do any of those things? Mr. Jones is the head of the marketing department. Doing any of these things will insult him. Then I will never get a promotion."

And so, Mr. Cohen just stood quietly and nodded his head as Mr. Jones spoke lashon hora.

"And you shall not flatter" (*Bamidbar* 35:33). The Ramban and the Sifrei explain that this verse is warning against flattering an evil person for your own selfish interests. By flattering his wicked deeds, you encourage him to do more evil. The Chafetz Chaim adds that there is a huge punishment for this sin. Because it defiles the Holy Land, it will ultimately result in exile.

> *Kinderlach . . .*
> *It is good to tell others good things about themselves. We all need recognition and appreciation. However, the praise must be sincere and from the heart. More importantly, it must be said for the good of the listener. This shows true caring and brings people closer together. Insincere, self-serving flattery is just the opposite. Kinderlach, make sure that your compliments come from the heart, and not just the lips.*

It Is Fair

"Avi dear, why are you crying?"

"It's not fair, Mommy."

"What is not fair?"

"He got away with stealing and did not get punished."

"What happened?"

"He stole a pencil from my schoolbag. The teacher did not see him."

"Calm down, Avi. Don't cry. You don't have to worry. Hashem is running the world. He rewards everyone for their good deeds, and punishes them for their sins. Just look in this week's parasha."

"I don't recall anything about stealing a pencil."

"Correct, Avi dear, but the Torah does speak about *arei miklat*, refuge cities, set aside to protect those people who accidentally killed someone. The killer had to flee from his home to the *ir miklat*. This exile, although it protected him from being killed by the victim's relatives, was also a punishment. Leaving his home, family, friends, and livelihood was very difficult in those days."

"Mommy, is that fair? Why did the victim have to die? What did he do wrong? And why did the killer have to flee? After all, it was only an accident. Where is Hashem's justice that you were speaking about?"

"Avi, the Gemara (*Makkos* 10b) explains what really happened. In a previous incident, one man had killed another intentionally, but there were no witnesses to convict him. He escaped punishment. And another man had killed someone accidentally, and there were no witnesses to convict him either. He also escaped the punishment of exile, or so it seemed.

"Hashem guided the events in such a way that these two men found themselves at the same inn one day. The former murder was sitting under a ladder and the one who had killed accidentally was climbing down the ladder. Suddenly, he fell on the other man and killed him. Witnesses saw the whole event."

"That was no coincidence."

"That is indeed what the Gemara says. The murder got the death penalty that he deserved. And the accidental killer got the exile that he deserved."

"So it is fair after all."

"Exactly."

Kinderlach . . .

"I'm going to teach him a lesson. He can't get away with that." Stop and think for a minute. In teaching him a lesson, are you going to do something that the Torah forbids? Are you going to take revenge? Are you going to speak lashon hora? *Are you going to hit him? Are you going to embarrass him? These things are all forbidden. "But he can't get away with that. He has to know that he did something wrong." That is correct. You should try to tell him in a way that is permissible. However, you should not try to punish him. That is not your job. Hashem is running the world. If the person deserves a punishment, he will get it. Hashem has many messengers. You do your job, and leave Hashem to do His job. That's the fair way.*

Simcha's Kinder Torah

Sefer Devarim

Parashas Devarim

Quit Stalling

"What a pity."

"What happened, Daddy?"

"Something that should have been very good."

"Did it turn out bad?"

"Not exactly. It just kept getting pushed off."

"Did it finally happen?"

"Yes, but it was not nearly as good as it could have been. If it had been taken care of right away, it would have been so much better."

"Daddy, you are so cryptic."

"Okay Avi, I won't put off telling you any longer."

"Great."

"The wonderful thing was a trip to the Land of Israel."

"Who? Where? When? Did someone we know win a free trip to Israel?"

"In a manner of speaking."

"Daddy, you are being cryptic again."

"Okay, Avi. I will tell you the whole story. It happened over three thousand years ago. The events are recounted in this week's parasha, *Devarim*."

"Aren't the first few verses of the parasha a review of some of the events of the history of the Jewish people, after the exodus from Egypt?"

"Very good, Avi. Verse six states that Hashem told us that we had spent enough time at Mt. Sinai after receiving the Torah."

"So where did He want us to go?"

"The Malbim explains that Hashem wanted us to go straight to the Land of Israel."

"Wow! We could have gone into the Land of Israel right after receiving the Torah."

"That's right, Avi. Many other great things would have happened. We would have gone straight, not the roundabout route. We would have conquered all of the lands promised to Avraham, which is much more than we actually received. But the biggest benefit of all, Avi, would have been the war."

"Which war?"

"Exactly. There would have been no need for a war to conquer the Land. Hashem would have handed it to us on a silver platter."

"Wow. So what happened? What held us up?"

"The Sin of the Golden Calf."

"Oh yes, now I remember. That happened on the seventeenth of Tammuz, at the end of Moshe Rabbeinu's time on Mt. Sinai. It was such a terrible sin that the Jewish people were not forgiven until Yom Kippur, 80 days later."

"I see that you know your Jewish history, Avi. What happened next?"

"They were given instructions to build the *Mishkan* (Tabernacle), and they indeed built it that winter. It was finished at Chanukah time. Then they were instructed to wait until the beginning of the month of Nissan, the month in which Pesach falls, to inaugurate the *Mishkan*."

"Excellent, Avi. They brought sacrifices to the *Mishkan* for three months; Hashem then gave them another opportunity to go directly into the Land of Israel. They had nothing to fear. The Land would be theirs without any wars."

"Great! I hope they took advantage this time."

"Unfortunately, they did not. They stalled again."

"Oh no. What happened?"

"They decided to send spies to scout out the Land."

"But Hashem already told them that it was a good land."

"True. They wanted to check it out themselves. Things were still okay until the spies came back with their report."

"I know what they said, Daddy. They said that the people in the Land were giants, too powerful to overcome."

"Right, Avi. That was *lashon hara* (derogatory speech) against Hashem and against the Land. This was a much worse sin. The punishment was forty years in the desert. The whole generation had to die there, and not enter the Land."

"That is so heartbreaking, Daddy."

"I know, Avi. It makes you want to cry. Do you know what day the spies came back with their report?"

"No, Daddy."

"Tisha B'Av. The Gemara (*Taanis* 29a) tells us Hashem's reaction to their complaints about the Land of Israel. 'This day you cried for no reason, therefore I will make this a day of crying for you throughout the generations.'"

"We still cry every Tisha B'Av, to this very day."

"That's right, Avi."

"What can we do about it, Daddy?"

"Hashem is ready to make this Tisha B'Av into a day of rejoicing for us, Avi."

"What is He waiting for?"

"Us. He wants us to correct our mistakes."

> *Kinderlach . . .*
> *Which mistakes was Avi's father speaking about? Mainly, the mistakes which caused the exile in the first place.* Lashon Hara *and* Sinas Chinam *(baseless hatred). When we learn to love all Jews, which brings us to never speak badly about them, this long exile will end. Kinderlach, we need to quit stalling. We stalled and put off entering the Holy Land. That is how we got into this mess. We need to quit stalling and enter the Holy Temple. May it be rebuilt speedily in our days. Amen.*

Because They Love You

The book of *Devarim* is the book of *tochacha* (constructive criticism). Moshe Rabbeinu, shortly before his death, gathered the Jewish people together and reviewed their mistakes over the past forty years. He also taught and reviewed the fundamentals of Jewish outlook, and of service of Hashem. Rav Shimshon Refael Hirsch comments that the first eleven chapters of the book of *Devarim* contain the foundations of love, fear, and cleaving to Hashem. Not only for that generation, but for all time.

Does anyone like to hear *tochacha*? We usually try to avoid it and we are not happy with the person who criticizes us. The *Da'as Zekeinim MiBaalei HaTosfos*, a commentary on the Torah, has a different outlook. "One who criticizes a person will later find favor in his eyes; more so than the one who unjustly praises him."

Moshe Rabbeinu criticized the Jewish people. Bilaam praised them. This is comparable to the son of a king who had two officers, one who loved him and one who hated him. The one who loved the son told him that he must obey the word of the king. If not, his father would have no mercy upon him. The other officer told him to do whatever he liked. After all, his father is the king. Nothing will happen to him. The first officer is like Moshe Rabbeinu, who spoke these words of *tochacha*. They have protected and guarded us for thousands of years. The second officer is like Bilaam, who said, "How good are your tents, Yaakov" — do whatever you like. You are Hashem's favorite nation and He will never punish you.

This commentary concludes by telling us that one who accepts *tochacha* will be blessed. The Jewish people were certainly willing to accept *tochacha*. How do we know that?

Rav Leib Chasman writes, in *Ohr Yahel*, that just a little hint of *tochacha* was enough for the Jewish people. The *tochacha* consisted merely of the name of the place where the sin occurred. Nothing more was necessary for them to get the point. The Midrash Rabba (*Devarim* 1:9) states: "Hashem said to Moshe, 'Since the Jewish people accepted the *tochacha*, you must bless them.' Immediately Moshe Rabbeinu blessed them. All who accept *tochacha* merit blessings."

Kinderlach . . .
When we make mistakes, Daddy and Mommy must correct us. Sometimes a word is enough, but at other times we need to hear more. It is not always pleasant to be criticized. When you think about it, you will realize that they are doing it because they love you. If not, they would just let you continue making mistakes. However, they love you and want the best for you. You also want the best for yourself. You also want the blessing promised those who accept criticism. Now doesn't that make it much easier to listen?

Parashas Va'eschanan

Call Me Any Time

"Can we go over the Gemara again?"
"Sure. Rava had a tremendous *kasha* (question) for Abaye."
"Right. How could two witnesses who are related . . ."

Ring, ring.
"What's that?"
"My cell phone. Excuse me one second."

The man is stunned as his study partner carries on a phone conversation in the middle of their learning session.

"I'm sorry about that interruption. Now, what were we learning? I can't seem to remember."
"It's not so easy to remember when there are interruptions."
"I need to have a cell phone in order that people can reach me at any time."
"I also have something that can reach someone at any time."

The man pulls a small brown object out of his pocket.

"What is that? Your cell phone?"

"In a manner of speaking. I can call and get through whenever I want."

"Really? What's the number?"

"100-20-1."

"What kind of a number is that? I never heard of such a number for a cell phone."

"Maybe you will recognize the number better in Hebrew. *Kuf-chof-aleph*. '*Shir LaMaalos. Esa einei el heharim, mei'ayin yavo ezri*' (A song of ascents. I raise my eyes up to the mountains. From where will my help come?)"

"Stop joking around. That's no cell phone in your hand. It is a book of *Tehillim*."

"I'm not joking. I can speak to Hashem whenever I want. I just open up this book and begin speaking. He hears every word. Just as He heard Moshe Rabbeinu's prayer in the beginning of the parasha."

Kinderlach . . .

Hashem's line is always open. Dial Him up whenever you want. Are you feeling a little down? Call His number. Are you a little nervous about a big test? He can help you. Are you scared about the state of security? Give Him a call to remind yourself that He is protecting you. Take your Tehillim with you at all times. Call Him 24 hours a day. His line is always open.

Sparkling Conversation

"Hi Chaim, how are you?"
"Great! How are you, Avi?"
"*Baruch Hashem.* Do you want to hear a really good word of Torah? I just learned it today."

"I do Avi, but may I ask you something first?"

"Sure, Chaim"

"Whenever we meet, you always have a word of Torah to tell me. How do you do it? Are you always preparing words of Torah for me? What's your secret?"

"Chaim, that's a good question. To answer it, I'm going to tell you another word of Torah."

"I might have known."

"In this week's parasha we find the first paragraph of the Shema, which we say every morning and night. We all know the words '*ViDibarta Bam*' of the Shema, which mean 'and you shall speak of them [words of Torah]' (*Devarim* 6:7). Rashi explains this verse with the words of the Sifrei: 'Make them (words of Torah) your main subject of conversation, and not just side talk.'

"If I am going to converse in Torah, then I must know what I am talking about. I need things to say, and they must be correct and clear in my mind. Therefore, whenever I learn something, I review it until I know it clearly and remember it. Then I am always prepared. When I meet you, I always have a word of Torah to share."

"That is fantastic, Avi. There are other benefits too.

Learning Torah is equal to all 613 mitzvos combined. For each word that you say, you get 613 mitzvos. Your word of Torah earns you thousands, even millions of mitzvos. Not only that, you avoid lashon hara while you are speaking words of Torah. And you avoid pointless conversation."

"Well said, Chaim. May you always be able to say such beautiful words."

"Amen."

Kinderlach . . .
Avi and Chaim said it all. Learn well so that you know and remember what you learned. And don't be bashful or afraid to share your learning with others. Become a sparkling Torah conversationalist. It will earn you many mitzvos and will spread beauty and peace in the world.

Guard Them

"Hi, Uncle Joe!"

"Hi, Avi. What brings you to my hardware store?"

"I was just walking this way with my friend Chaim, and we decided to stop in. Uncle Joe, how many different items do you have in stock in the store?"

"About 2500, Avi."

"How much does this monkey wrench cost?"

"$12.49."

"How about this tube of glue?"
"69 cents."

Avi goes on and asks him the prices of eight other items and Uncle Joe knows them all cold. Down to the penny.

"Uncle Joe, do you know the prices of all 2500 items?"
"You bet, Avi."
"Wow!"
"Prices are very important, boys. When people want to buy something, they want to know the price. They don't want to wait around until I look it up in the book."
"How do you memorize all of the prices?"
"There is only one way. I just keep going over them until I know them."

"Guard yourself and guard your soul very well, lest you forget these things that your eyes saw" (*Devarim* 4:9): guard yourself from forgetting words of Torah that you once learned (*Pirkei Avos* 3:8). Why does a person forget his learning? The Torah Temima explains that a person who is too lazy to review properly will forget. Why? The Torah is not important enough to commit to memory. Therefore, he just lets it slip away.

> *Kinderlach . . .*
> *The items in Uncle Joe's hardware store are very important to him. They are his livelihood. Therefore he makes sure that he knows them. The Torah that we learn is much more important than a livelihood. It keeps the whole world running and protects us from our enemies. How can we even think of forgetting it? There is only one way to remember. Review over and over, and over and over again. Vacation is a wonderful time to review. Take advantage of it. You'll have no regrets.*

Constant Mitzvos

"What are you doing, Avi?"

"I'm doing three mitzvos."

"Really! Three mitzvos! It looks like you are not doing anything."

"These mitzvos do not require action, only thought."

"Which mitzvos are you doing?"

"They are all in this week's parasha. Knowing that Hashem exists, knowing that He is one, and loving Him."

"How do you do those mitzvos?"

"Well, Avraham Avinu looked at the world and saw beautiful mountains, valleys, rivers, and oceans. He wondered, 'How can this wonderful world keep going by itself? There must be Someone running it.' By process of trial and error, he concluded that Hashem created and is running the world, and that He is only One. We can look at the same extraordinary world and appreciate that Hashem created it and He alone is running it."

"We also have the Torah. The Sefer HaChinuch explains that the first paragraph of the Shema tells us how to love Hashem. 'And you shall love Hashem your God with all of your heart, with all of your soul, and with all of your might.' How? 'Place these words which I command you today upon your heart' (*Devarim* 6:5–6). By learning the Torah, and thinking about what you learned, you will come to know The One who spoke and created the world. Knowing and appreciating Hashem's Torah will lead you to knowing and appreciating Hashem."

Kinderlach . . .
You can do these mitzvos while you are playing, resting, walking to school, or eating. Just take the time to think about Hashem's wonderful world. And review some of the Torah that you learned today. Just imagine: you can do mitzvos every minute of the day. Isn't that great?

Parashas Eikev

Who Did All Of This?

"Please come in. Make yourself comfortable in my beautiful new home. Let me show you some of my most prized possessions. Do you like the plush carpets? I imported them from Persia. I bought the handcrafted furniture in Italy and it is very expensive. What about the custom kitchen cabinets? I hired the best carpenter to make them. The handles are gold-plated. Do you like my exotic houseplants? My gardener imported them from the four corners of the world. Please relax and enjoy everything. I want you to appreciate the beautiful home that I built."

This man is making a very big mistake. He thinks that he did everything. He uses the words, "I, me, and my" in almost every sentence! The Torah warns us against this very thing. "And you will say in your heart, 'My strength and the might of my hand made all of this wealth for me'" (*Devarim* 8:17). A person can forget all about Hashem and think that his own skills, talents, and hard work are solely responsible for all of his wealth and accomplishments. How did this man get to the point where he made such a mistake?

Actually, we should ask how **we** can avoid making the same mistake. The Torah tells us: "You will eat and you will be satisfied, and bless Hashem your God, for the good Land that He gave you" (*Devarim* 8:10). This is the source of the mitzvah to bless Hashem after we eat a bread meal. Rabbeinu Bechaye shares a practical insight with us: we have a mitzvah to bless Hashem. Think about this for a minute. Does He really need our blessing? Quite the opposite! He is the source of all blessing. Why, then, are we blessing Him? It is for our own good. We need to remind ourselves that He is the One who gives us all of the good things that we are privileged to enjoy in this world.

The next seven verses warn the Jewish people against forgetting Hashem. "Take care lest you forget Hashem your God . . ." (*Devarim* 8:11). The Yalkut Shimoni explains the juxtaposition of these verses as follows. Wherever the Torah mentions eating to satisfaction, it warns against forgetting Hashem. Being well fed and satisfied can easily lead to overlooking the source of the prosperity. That is why we are commanded to bless Hashem precisely at the point when we are in the greatest danger of forgetting Him.

Kinderlach . . .
Isn't Mommy's food great? So delicious and nutritious. It is so yummy that we always swallow every bite. Now it is time to go to school. Hurry up, the school bus is leaving in five minutes. No time to waste. Say the Bircas HaMazone *(Grace after Meals) quickly, and get going. Hmmm. Is this the way to thank someone? If we had just received a new toy from Uncle Max we would surely call him on the telephone and thank him many times for his generosity. What about Hashem? Doesn't He deserve a proper thank-you? Hashem wants us to thank Him so that we do not forget that He is the One who provided this delicious meal. So, don't swallow your blessings along with your food. Take the time to say* Bircas HaMazone *clearly and with meaning.*

Built To Last

"Did you hear about the terrible tragedy?"
"Oh no."
"Something that was standing in this world for 123 years is no more."
"I'm almost afraid to ask."
"It was magnificent. Hundreds of thousands of man-hours of work went into this project. It was under construction day and night. No effort was spared."
"When was it finished?"
"It was never fully finished until its demise. It was always

being constantly improved."

"You've really got my curiosity aroused. Why didn't I hear about this on the news? What was it? Please tell me."

"A tzaddik died. The Torah recounts the death of Aharon HaKohen in this week's parasha (*Devarim* 10:6)."

"What? The death of a tzaddik? What sort of a construction project is that? I thought that you were referring to a building, a bridge, or a tunnel."

"A tzaddik is a much bigger 'construction project' than any of those things. Do you know how many hours a tzaddik must learn Torah in order to become a sage? Day and night for years and years upon end. Hundreds of thousands of man-hours of work. That dwarfs the amount of work put into any mere building or bridge."

"I never thought about it like that."

"A tzaddik benefits all of those who come to him: to learn, seek advice, or gather spiritual strength. He is called the pillar of the world. He is a paragon of wisdom, kindness, and good character traits. What a magnificent spiritual edifice."

"I'm going to cry. His death was truly a tragedy."

"Let me comfort you. He is still standing. He is more permanent than any bridge or building. Even after his body dies, his soul lives on forever in the next world. His teachings will endure even in this world."

"May we all learn from them."

"Amen."

> *Kinderlach . . .*
> *Let us appreciate tzaddikim while they are still alive. Go to tzaddikim to learn Torah and ask questions. Observe how they conduct themselves in a most humble and dignified manner. Ask them for blessings for success in all areas of life. Help them in any way that you can. Appreciate what a truly precious gift Hashem has given to us.*

Trust The Boss

"You look like you are working pretty hard, Sam."

"I am. This is a good job, and I want to do it well."

"Are you getting paid well?"

"*B'ezras Hashem* (With Hashem's help)."

"Why do you say that? Have you gotten paid yet?"

"No, not yet."

"Are you sure that you will get paid?"

"Sure. My contract says that I will get paid at the end of the job."

"Do you place your faith in that contract?"

"Of course."

"And it will be '*eikev*' your listening to these laws [of the Torah] and guarding them, and performing them; and Hashem will keep [His part] of the covenant which He made and swore to your forefathers" (*Devarim* 7:12). The Baal HaTurim interprets *eikev* as "at the end." The previous verse (at the end of *Parashas Va'eschanan*) states that we must perform the mitzvos today. The Torah follows up by informing us that the reward will not come until the end of a person's life.

> *Kinderlach . . .*
> *We can be as happy and confident as Sam, the worker in the story. We will receive a big, big reward for all of the hard work that we have put into Hashem's mitzvos. When? At the end of the job. Some people might ask, "Are you sure that you will get paid?" To this we answer, "We have nothing to worry about. We have the contract to prove it. The Torah."*

Parashas Re'eh

Take Care Of Each Other

"Everyone please quiet down. Grandpa is about to make Kiddush."

"Thank you, Grandma. Before I begin, I would just like to say something. Tonight is Rosh Hashanah, the beginning of a new year. We all hope that Hashem will bless us this year, as every year, with good health, prosperity, and success in all areas."

"Amen."

"The whole family is gathered together, so I want to take this opportunity to say just one thing to all of you. We do not know what Hashem has in store for us this year, or any other year. Some of you may prosper, some not. Some may fall on hard times. I just ask one thing of you. If one of your brothers or sisters does need help, I would like the rest of you to take care of him. If he needs a loan, lend him money. If he can't pay back, give him a gift. If he is working for you, treat him nicely. If he gets into trouble, help him out of it. Always think about your brothers and sisters. If you listen to these words, I promise you one thing. I will always take care of you. You may not know this, but I am a very influential person. I have many, many connections. I can and will take care of you."

"You shall surely give to him (your destitute brother) and you shall not feel badly in your heart because you gave to him (*Devarim* 15:10)." "You shall surely give a tenth of your crop [to the poor and to the Levi]" (*Devarim* 14:22). "Do not forsake the Levi who is in your cities" (*Devarim* 14:27). "The Levi . . . the convert, the orphan, and the widow in your gates will come and eat and be satisfied. In order that Hashem your God will bless you in all your handiwork" (*Devarim* 14:29). "Guard yourself lest you forsake the Levi" (*Devarim* 12:19). "If you make My [Levi, convert, orphan, and widow] happy, I [Hashem] will make your [son, daughter, servant, and handmaid] happy" (*Rashi, Devarim* 16:11).

The parasha is full of reminders to remember our less fortunate brothers. Hashem promises big blessings for those who take care of their fellow Jews. Why? "You are Hashem's children" (*Devarim* 14:1). We are all His children. Just like the grandpa in the story, everyone wants to see his children take care of each other. That is his greatest source of satisfaction.

Kinderlach . . .
Hashem is our Father and we are His children. He wants us to help each other. Step one is to see another Jew as your brother. Of course you will help your brother. You cannot bear to see him suffer. He is your flesh and blood. Kinderlach, we are all part of a very special family called Klal Yisrael, *the Jewish people. We all love each other, and we all take care of each other.*

Hashem's Children

"You are children to Hashem, your God—you shall not cut yourselves and you shall not make a bald spot between your eyes when mourning" (*Devarim* 14:1). Tearing the skin in time of mourning was a barbaric custom practiced by the nations of the world. In the same verse, the Torah reminds us that we are Hashem's children, and commands us not to follow this custom. What is the connection between these two ideas?

The *Da'as Zekeinim MiBaalei HaTosfos* explain that the custom of tearing the skin in mourning was an expression of despair about the future. The child was now alone in the world without a father. However, the Jewish people are different. We are Hashem's children and He is our Father. He is alive and well, and we have no reason to despair.

The Ohr HaChaim HaKadosh and the S'forno have a different angle on this question. People despair in mourning because they think that their loved one is gone. However, we know that this world is only temporary. Hashem sends His children down here for a short time, and then He calls them back. They return to their Father, Who is the source of all life. The life that they are now living in the next world is nicer than all of the pleasures of this world.

> *Kinderlach . . .*
> *We are Hashem's children. He loves us as a Father loves his child. He wants to be close to us, and He wants us to be close to Him. We are now at the beginning of the month of Elul. The letters of the word Elul form the acronym of the verse* Ani LiDodi ViDodi Li, *"I am my Beloved's and my Beloved is mine" (Shir HaShirim 6:3). This describes the depth of the relationship that we are capable of having with Hashem. This month is a golden opportunity. Hashem makes Himself available and comes close to us in Elul. Seize the opportunity. Get close to Him.*

Togetherness

The Gemara (*Yevamos* 14a) relates an additional interpretation of this verse. Although *"tisgodedu"* means to make a cut in the skin, it also means *"aguda"*, "bundle or group." Therefore *"lo tisgodedu"* means: "Do not break yourselves up into groups." The Torah is warning the Rabbinical courts against creating divisions among people. (The details of this *halachah* are beyond the scope of *Simcha's Kinder Torah*.) The Rambam writes that this could cause major disputes.

Perhaps this idea is also related to the first half of the verse. "You are Hashem's children"—do not create disputes among yourselves. What pains a parent most is to see his children fighting. When we remember that we are all Hashem's children, we want to give Him satisfaction, not anguish. Therefore we want to make peace, not fights. One of the main ways to serve Hashem in this month of Elul is to promote unity among the Jewish people.

> *Kinderlach . . .*
> *The King is coming. We crown Hashem as our King this Rosh Hashanah. However, there is no King without a nation, and there is no nation without unity. We are His nation and He is our King. However, our relationship is even deeper than that. As we say in our prayers,* **Avinu** *Malkeinu ("Our* **Father***, Our King"). He is our Father and we are His children. How can the children even dream of fighting in the presence of the Father?*

Parashas Shoftim

Assign Responsibility

"What happened? Why are the chairs and tables not set up?"

"I don't know."

"Whose job was it?"

"As I remember, at the last meeting we never really assigned jobs. We just made a list of tasks, and assumed that people would take responsibility and finish the job."

"That was a big mistake. The Torah realized the faultiness of this logic."

"Really?"

"Yes. It is a mitzvah in this week's parasha. The *Kohanim* and the *Leviim* had fixed weeks of service in the *Beis HaMikdash*. Each of the 24 groups would serve one week."

"Why?"

"The Sefer HaChinuch explains that any task that is assigned to a specific individual or individuals will get done. However, if the job is vaguely left to a group of people, sometimes only a few will do a little of the work, or some people will refuse all but a certain type of work. Laziness and despair can then take root, and the job will never be completed."

Kinderlach . . .

The wisdom of our Torah is endless. It even guides us how to get the job done. We can use this wisdom on Erev Shabbos. Mommy can make a written list of all of the jobs that need to be done to prepare for Shabbos. Then each of the kinderlach can write their name next to the job or jobs that they will do. When you finish the job, you can put a big check mark next to your name. I am sure that the preparations will go very smoothly, and the family will arrive at the Shabbos table relaxed and happy.

The First

"Young man. May I help you?"
"Yes sir. I'd like to pay for these items."
"With pleasure, young man."

The store owner began ringing up the items on his cash register. The young man noticed something unusual on the wall behind the register. He looked closer. It was a framed receipt for a tsedaka donation.

"Excuse me sir, may I ask you something?"
"Go ahead young man."
"Why did you frame that tsedaka receipt and hang it on the wall?"

"That donation, young man, was from the first dollar that I ever made. I dreamed for years about opening this store. I scrimped and saved and borrowed until I could finally go into business. I bought this store building, but it was a mess. I renovated, painted the walls and set up the shelves with my own two hands. Finally it was finished. I ordered the merchandise and stocked the shelves. I opened the doors and the first customer walked in. He bought a pair of socks for a dollar and paid for them. After all of my hard work, that first dollar meant so much to me. Hashem had blessed me with my own store. I returned that dollar to Him by giving it to charity."

"The first of your grain, wine, and oil and the first of the shearing of your flock you shall give to Him (Devarim 18:4)". The Sefer HaChinuch explains that it is fitting to remember the One Who blessed us with prosperity. A person works hard sowing and reaping his crops. When he sees the fruits of his labor, he wants to enjoy them. Remember Hashem first, before you take for yourself.

Kinderlach . . .

We all work hard. If we merit, Hashem blesses us with success. That is the time to remember Him. Did you get a gift for your birthday? Before you spend anything, take some and give it to tsedaka. Did you earn some money babysitting? Don't forget about the poor people. Did you win a prize? Give something to those who learn Torah. They are supporting you. You can support them. At all times of blessing and success, remember that Hashem blessed you with this prosperity. Return the first to Him.

Good Habits

"Avi, it's time to get up. You don't want to be late for *shacharis* (morning prayers).
"Okay, Mommy. But *shacharis* begins in half an hour."
"Avi, It's always good to be early."

Later that day...
"Avi, begin preparing to leave. We must catch the bus."
"Yes, Mommy. But the bus leaves in twenty minutes."
"Avi, It's always good to be early."

That evening...
"Avi, it's time to begin getting ready for bed."
"Mommy, bedtime is not for another fifteen minutes. You are always telling me to be early. Why?"
"Avi dear, being early has many advantages. A person who is early is relaxed, because he is not hurrying to make his appointments. He does not forget things in the last-minute rush. He has time to collect his thoughts when he arrives. One who is early for prayers, prays better because his mind is settled. An early bird can be more patient when things go wrong, because they will not make him miss his appointment. He improves the quality of whatever he does because he is more relaxed."
"I never realized that, Mommy."
"I'm trying to help you develop a good habit, Avi. It will help you the rest of your life."
"Thank you, Mommy. You always help me. We learned

about developing good habits yesterday in out parasha class."

"That is so interesting, Avi. Where does the parasha mention good habits?"

"The very first mitzvah, Mommy. 'Judges and officers make for yourselves in all of your gates" (Devarim 16:18). The Sefer HaChinuch explains that the judges and officers enforced the Torah laws, making sure that people always did the right thing. They developed good habits. Habit becomes a person's 'second nature'. He learns to naturally do only good. This leads to following Torah laws out of love of Hashem, and not fear of officers."

"Fascinating, Avi. Daddy once told me that a great Rav once said that things that his parents were strict about in his childhood were now easy for him. On the other hand, things that they did not stress were still a struggle for him to this very day."

"Wow."

"That is the power of habit."

Kinderlach . . .

Now is the time to develop good habits. Punctuality, patience, happiness, good learning habits, politeness, good eating habits, and respect are all a matter of habit. Second nature comes easier when you are young. Work on these things now. Also, thank Daddy and Mommy when they help you shape your habits. They are giving you a gift for life.

Parashas Ki Seitzei

Lost and Found

"Whew, we just made the bus."

"It's a good thing, too. We would have had to wait half an hour for the next one."

"We really are fortunate, getting right off the first bus and now catching this second bus."

"How much money do I owe you?"

"Three shekels."

"Okay, I have it right here in my wallet. Where is my wallet? It's not in my pocket. Let me check through all of my pockets. Oy vey, I don't have it. It must have dropped out of my pocket as we were hurrying off the first bus."

"Quickly, let's write down the number of the bus. We can call the bus company's lost-and-found department."

"We can try, but there was a lot of money in that wallet. I hope the finder will be kind enough to give it to the lost-and-found."

The next day the two friends meet again . . .
"Look at this!"
"Is that your wallet?"
"Yes it is."

"Where did you find it?"

"At the bus company's lost-and-found. The driver apparently found it on my seat and handed it in."

"How about the money?"

"It was all still in the wallet."

"*Chasdei Hashem* (Hashem's kindness). It makes me feel like crying from joy. See what a holy nation the Jewish people is. The Torah commands us to return lost objects—and we do it. No questions asked. The finder could have kept all of the money and no one would have known. Aren't you happy that he turned it in?"

"I certainly am. I truly appreciate what the Sefer HaChinuch (*Mitzvah* 538) wrote about the mitzvah of returning lost objects. Forgetting things is very common. This mitzvah enables a person's lost or forgotten objects to be watched safely by his fellow Jew. It is as if they were still in the owner's possession. The owner feels great relief and happiness from this. As it is written in *Tehillim* (19:9): 'The statutes of Hashem are straight, they make the heart happy.'"

Kinderlach . . .

Do you remember the last time that you lost something? Do you remember the bad feeling that you had? You might never see your lost object again. When it was returned to you, do you remember how happy and grateful you felt? Just imagine the tremendous happiness that you are giving someone when you return his lost object. Don't miss the opportunity to make someone happy.

Family Gratitude

"Hurry up children, we only have a few minutes left. Chavi, finish setting the table. Avi, sweep the floor. Shoshie, Esti, finish getting dressed. Mommy, is the food ready?"

"Daddy, why does everything have to be so nice?"

"Because Mr. Goldberg is coming."

"Oh, Mr. Goldberg. We work so hard for Mr. Goldberg. Why?"

"Esti, every year around this time, Mr. Goldberg comes here to Israel to visit. We are honored to have him as a guest in our house."

"But Daddy, we treat him like a VIP."

"He is a very important person to our family. Do you want to know why?"

"Yes, we want to know why we are working so hard to make things nice for him."

"Many years ago, my great-grandfather and Mr. Goldberg's great-grandfather were friends in Russia. Those were dangerous times for Jews. My great-grandfather was captured by the Cossacks and thrown into prison. Mr. Goldberg's great-grandfather risked his life to get my great-grandfather out of prison. Were it not for him, my great-grandfather would have died a young man in prison, and none of us would be here today."

"Wow!"

"Now do you see why we give Mr. Goldberg the red-carpet treatment?"

"We sure do, Daddy."

"An Ammonite or a Moavite shall not enter into the congregation of Hashem . . . because they did not greet you with bread and water on the road when you were leaving Egypt, and because they hired Bilaam to curse you" (*Devarim* 23:4–5). The Ramban explains that Avraham Avinu risked his life to save Lot and his wife from the four kings. Lot was the patriarch of the nations of Ammon and Moav. Therefore, these nations owe their very existence to Avraham and his descendants. They should have expressed their gratitude to the Jewish people and treated them kindly. Instead, they responded nastily. Because they carry this negative character trait, even their converts may not marry into our nation.

Kinderlach . . .

We learn two important lessons from this. One is that we must show our gratitude to those who have helped us. Parents, teachers, brothers, or neighbors who have done nice things for us all deserve our appreciation. Secondly, we must realize that we are part of a family. We are also grateful for good deeds done for other members of our family. If you help my brother, you help me. The Jewish people are all really one big family. We are all descendants of Avraham. When we help each other, we help ourselves. And we appreciate every good deed done for every Jew.

Compassion

"You shall not muzzle an ox while it is threshing" (*Devarim* 25:4). Threshing is separating wheat from the husks. This was done by stepping on the wheat. The husks get split off and are left behind. People used oxen to step on the wheat. We may not muzzle the ox, thereby preventing it from eating the wheat while it is threshing, because the ox gets hungry while working. To stop him from eating would be cruel. The Sefer HaChinuch (*Mitzvah* 596) explains the reason behind this mitzvah: we should train ourselves to be compassionate. If we accustom ourselves to always being kind and benevolent, even with animals, we will surely be compassionate with people.

Kinderlach . . .

A person can work on a good character trait in many ways. Kindness to animals is related to kindness to people. The Torah teaches us that how we treat people is more important than how we treat animals. But that does not mean that we may be cruel to animals. We should look at it the other way. We must be kind even to animals—how much more so to people!

Safety

"You shall make a fence around your roof" (*Devarim* 22:8). The Sefer HaChinuch (*Mitzvah* 546) speaks about how Hashem is always supervising our lives and how He decrees everything that happens to us. Still, a person must guard himself from dangerous situations. Hashem decreed that fire will burn, and water will extinguish fire. A falling rock will smash a person, and a person who falls from a high roof will die. Hashem breathed our souls into our bodies and gave us the wisdom we need to guard ourselves. He then placed us among the elements, subjected us to the laws of nature, and commanded us to guard ourselves from dangerous situations. The exceptions are those chosen tzaddikim like Avraham Avinu, who could allow himself to be thrown into a fiery furnace and still live. The rest of us must guard ourselves from danger.

Kinderlach . . .
Fences were erected to protect people from falling. They are not meant for climbing. The jungle gym in the park is for climbing. A thrown rock can hurt someone very badly. A wound inflicted with a metal object is serious enough to break Shabbos to treat it. A car, traveling at even the slowest speed, is so big and heavy that it will hurt someone very badly. A person can drown in the shallowest water. Firecrackers are so dangerous that they are illegal in many places. . . .

. . . . Hashem wants you to take care of yourself. He gave you a wonderful body and put a beautiful soul into it. He wants you to do mitzvos with that body and soul. How can you do mitzvos properly if you are hurt? We know that Hashem protects all of us. He gives extra protection to His special tzaddikim. We still must protect ourselves. We fulfill His wishes by properly caring for the body that He gave us.

Parashas Ki Savo

The Happy Mitzvos

"Oy! Shabbos is coming."

"Oy? Why do you say 'oy' Mrs. Kvetch?"

"Because there is so much work to do before Shabbos. Cook the food, wash the dishes, make the beds, wash the floors, bathe everyone, dress them in Shabbos clothes, set the table, prepare the candles, the list is endless. Oy!"

"Hmmm . . . I see. You are missing a very big point, Mrs. Kvetch."

"Really? What is that?"

"Shabbos is a tremendous gift from Hashem to the Jewish people. When observed properly, it is a day of total spiritual and physical pleasures a bit of the World to Come. Besides all of the enjoyment in this world, we get unfathomable reward in the Next World for keeping the mitzvos of Shabbos. Shabbos is fantastic!"

"You are right. I am missing the point. I got too caught up in negative thoughts."

The next day . . .

"Oy! I have to go to school."

"Oy? Why do you say 'oy', Chaim?"

"I have to get up out of bed, dress, pack my schoolbag, catch the bus, pray, eat breakfast. Then, if I have any strength left, I have to learn for three hours, and sit in class and listen for another hour. Oy!"

"Hmmm . . . I see. You are missing a very big point, Chaim."

"Really? What is that?"

"The Mishnah states, *'Talmud Torah kineged kulam'* (Peah 1:1) - each word of Torah that you learn is equal to all 613 mitzvos combined. Each mitzvah gives you unbelievable blessing in this world, and unimaginable reward in the next world. Not only that, the Orchos Tzaddikim writes that the reward done for a mitzvah *b'simcha* (with happiness) is one thousand times greater than a mitzvah performed unhappily. You should be ecstatic over every word of Torah that you learn."

"You are right. I am missing the point. I got too caught up in negative thoughts."

"Because you did not serve Hashem, your God, amid gladness and goodness of heart when everything was abundant" (Devarim 28:47). The Torah elaborates a long list of curses, misfortunes, and tragedies that will befall the Jewish people. Why? Because we did not serve Hashem with happiness. Happiness is a prerequisite to proper *avodat Hashem*. And the true happiness is the enjoyment of doing Hashem's mitzvos.

> *Kinderlach . . .*
> *Dovid HaMelech revealed the secret thousands of years ago. "Serve Hashem with happiness. Come before Him rejoicing." (Tehillim 100:2). We are ecstatic to serve Hashem. Time to pray? Wonderful! An opportunity to serve Hashem. Shabbos preparations or cleanup? Fantastic! I'm serving Hashem! Time to learn Torah? I love it! I'm serving Hashem . . . with simcha!*

The War

"Men, prepare yourselves for the most difficult battle that you have ever fought."

"How tough can it be, officer? We have fought many wars and won them all."

"Men, this enemy is different. Normally when you defeat an enemy, he surrenders and you have won the war. This enemy never gives up. You can defeat him one hundred or even one thousand times, yet he will never give up."

"It sound like an impossible mission, sir."

"It would be impossible for our army alone. However, we have a very powerful ally who will help us in this war."

"Who is it? A member of the UN? A mercenary army?"

"No, our ally is . . . Hashem. And our enemy is the *Yetzer Hara.*"

The Ohr HaChaim HaKadosh has a beautiful explanation of the verses (Devarim 26:5-10) that were recited when bringing the *bikurim* (first fruits). They are a description of the war against the *yetzer hara*. Verse seven states, "And we cried out to Hashem." This hints to the fact that we must pray to Hashem every day, asking Him to save us from the *yetzer hara*. The verse continues, "And Hashem heard our voices." Although He created the *yetzer hara* to test us, when we cry to Him in prayer, He will give us the strength to defeat it.

> *Kinderlach . . .*
> *Selichos are approaching. These prayers are a wonderful opportunity to cry out to Hashem and ask for His assistance. Realize that the yetzer hara has often defeated you, making you err. Appeal to Hashem for help in beating the enemy. Then you will receive assistance from our Ally above—and win the war.*

Pray for Me Too

"Then we cried out to Hashem, the God of our forefathers and Hashem heard our voice" (Devarim 26:7). The Chafetz Chaim explains that we should cry out to Hashem in prayer during times of trouble. The request should be made on behalf of the entire Jewish people. It should also be made after we have performed a mitzvah. The Chafetz Chaim often repeated the advice given to us by our sages when praying for a sick person. We should include him "amongst other sick ones of Israel." When comforting mourners we should comfort them "amongst the other mourners of Israel." Hashem will more readily accept a prayer offered on behalf of the nation that a prayer for an individual. The person is not alone. He is a member of the Jewish people. It is easy to turn away a single person. A whole nation cannot be denied.

Kinderlach . . .
The Chafetz Chaim give us a key to making our prayers more meaningful and effective. Praying for fellow Jews who are suffering. We probably all know of someone who is in need of special prayers. We also have our own personal requests. We should include them all in our prayers. Make sure that you pray as our sages say, "amongst the nation of Israel." Besides making your prayers more effective, it will make you feel more empathetic with other Jews who are suffering. Help your friend. Pray for him.

Parashas Nitzavim

The Road Back

"Now we are really lost. It is pitch black and there are no road signs. We lost our map, and there is not a living soul here to ask for directions. What shall we do?"

"First of all, let's not panic. There is a way to deal with every problem. Let us open up the *Chumash*."

"What? The *Chumash*? We are in a life-and-death situation! What are you doing reading the *Chumash*?"

"Listen to what it says in this week's parasha. The Jewish people will be dispersed among all of the nations. If you are at the very ends of heaven, from there Hashem will gather you in."

"That is wonderful. I hope that we are alive to experience it. In the meantime, what do we do now?"

"You shall return and listen to the voice of Hashem and perform all of His commandments."

"I am ready to do *t'shuva* (repent). Maybe that will save us."

"Our situation is a parable to the *Chumash*. Do you remember how we cried so bitterly on Tisha B'Av? We cried over the long, bitter *golus* (exile) and the lack of direction. We are all wandering around in a spiritual darkness with no one to guide our way. What can we do? We are lost . . . spiritually lost."

"I am going to start crying again. Really, what can we do?"

"The answer is also in the parasha. 'For this commandment [of *t'shuva*] is not hidden from you, and it is not far away. It is not in heaven . . . nor is it across the sea . . . Rather the matter is very near to you—in your mouth and in your heart—to perform it' (*Devarim* 30:11-14). Don't you see that there is nothing that can prevent us from doing *t'shuva?*"

"I'm still not convinced."

"The Malbim explains that an animal will never do anything to harm itself. Why, then, does a human being, who has intelligence, do sins which will surely harm him?"

"Excellent question."

"Because our hearts are stopped up. The healthy heart will always guide the person in the proper direction. Our hearts are covered with layers of spiritual grime, preventing our true feelings from shining forth. *T'shuva* is removing the layers covering our hearts. Even in this deep, dark *golus* we need no guide other than our hearts to return to Hashem."

"Hashem, please save us! I will do my best to listen to my heart and keep Your mitzvos!"

A car slowly approaches from the distance. The two men flag down the car. Inside is a search team. As the two men board the car, they radio to headquarters that the lost men have been found. The man in the back seat is sobbing uncontrollably, his heart breaking.

"Thank you, Hashem. Thank you for everything!"

> *Kinderlach . . .*
> *How many times has Hashem saved us? From illness, from poverty, and from danger. Why does he place us in a dangerous situation, then save us? One of the reasons is that He wants us to recognize that He is the One Who saved us. And He wants us to thank Him. The best way to thank Him is by doing t'shuva. When we keep His mitzvos, it gives Him pleasure. It is also good for us, because we become closer to Him. Now is the time for t'shuvah, kinderlach. Take the opportunity.*

Wealthy Forever

"Daddy, that is a magnificent home. Just the gardens alone are worth more than our house."

"Avi, I know the owner personally."

"Really? He must be a very wealthy man."

"I knew him before he was rich. He had a regular job. However, he had a burning ambition to be rich. He saved all of his salary money, and lived like a poor man. In a few years, he bought a business. He continued to live very poorly, putting all of the profits back into the business. The business grew and he became very wealthy. Now he no longer has to live like a poor man."

"He was willing to be poor temporarily in order to have long-term wealth."

"Exactly, Avi."

"The Chafetz Chaim speaks along similar lines, Daddy."

"I cannot believe that the holy Chafetz Chaim advocates amassing a fortune of money, Avi."

"No, Daddy. He advises us to amass a fortune of Torah."

"Now that sounds more like the Chafetz Chaim."

"He writes in his commentary on Parashas Nitzavim that the only fortune to be earned in this world is the Torah."

"It is not in heaven" (*Devarim* 30:12). There is no Torah in heaven. Torah was given to be learned down here, to purify our souls. Without the Torah, we would be poor forever. When we learn Torah, we amass a great fortune. Even if we are poor in this world, it is only temporary. Like the man in the story, who was willing to undergo temporary poverty to acquire great wealth. Torah riches are beyond comprehension.

Kinderlach . . .
Now is the time to work hard. You will have plenty of time to enjoy your Torah fortune later. However, you only have a short amount of time to work at learning Torah. Do not waste even one minute. Fabulous wealth awaits you.

Together As One

"Avi, why are you limping?"

"I have a sore on my little toe. Every step hurts so much. I can't even walk straight. My whole leg hurts because I am walking crooked. I am off-balance and my back hurts too. All these pains are giving me a headache."

"Oy vey, that's terrible! Who would have ever thought that from one little toe, your whole body can hurt. The toe seems so small and insignificant . . . until it begins to hurt."

"That's the way it is, Chaim. All of the parts of our body are interconnected. If the smallest limb or organ is not working properly, the whole body is affected."

"Avi, believe it or not, you have given me a whole new insight on this week's parasha."

"Please share it with me, Chaim."

"It says, 'For you to pass into the *b'ris* (covenant) of Hashem . . .' (*Devarim* 29:11). The word 'you' is in the singular form, yet the rest of the parasha is written in the plural form. The K'li Yakar explains that the singular from of 'you' is an indication that this covenant was different from the others.

"This was a covenant of unity among the Jewish people. At that point in time, each and every Jew became responsible for his fellow man, and from then on, the deeds of each one of us affects the entire nation. Our Sages describe this as: 'All Jews are responsible for one another' (*Shevu'os* 39a). The K'li Yakar describes the Jewish nation as one body. When one limb is injured, the whole body feels it. Similarly when one Jew sins, it affects all of us."

> *Kinderlach . . .*
> *"All Jews are responsible for one another." What does this mean? If my friend is having a hard time, I should help him. If my friend needs to borrow something, I should lend it to him. If he needs help studying, I should learn with him. These are the types of things that promote unity among the Jewish people. Kinderlach, national unity is one of the main goals of Rosh Hashanah. Do your part. Take the responsibility to help others.*

Parashas Vayelech

Everyone Is Going

"Do I really have to go, Daddy?"
"Yes, Avi."
"Who else is going?"
"The whole family—Mommy and I, and all of your brothers and sisters."
"What about Grandpa and Grandma?"
"They are going also."
"Uncle Aaron and Aunt Rachel?"
"Yes, along with their children."
"What about the next-door neighbors?"
"They are all going. Even the little infants and their great-grandfather."
"Everybody on our street?"
"Of course."
"Is there anyone who is not going?"
"Not that I know of."
"But why? It must be a very important event if everyone is going."
"It is. Once every seven years, the entire Jewish nation—men, women, and children—gathers together on the second day of Succos, in the Beis HaMikdash."

"What do they do over there?"

"They listen."

"That's good. You always tell me that it is important to listen. What do they listen to?"

"Words of Torah, from the beginning of the Book of Devarim."

"But we just read the beginning of Devarim two months ago, in shul. Didn't they hear it then?"

"Okay, Avi. I will tell you the whole story. We are going to perform a very important mitzvah called *Hakhel,* "gathering together." The Sefer HaChinuch explains that we gather the entire Jewish nation together to perform this mitzvah. The foundation of our nation is the Torah. It is what separates us from the other nations. It is our glory and our greatness. It guarantees us a wonderful life, in both this world and the next. Therefore, it is only fitting that we gather everyone together to hear these words of Torah. This demonstrates its supreme importance. In addition, this fills everyone's heart with a tremendous desire to learn Torah. From learning Torah, they will come to know Hashem, and merit to receive all of His goodness."

"Wow. It really is important to go. I want to be a part of this national mitzvah. When everyone gets together, I want to be there."

> Kinderlach . . .
> What is the most important thing in our lives? The Torah. We have no mitzvah of Hakhel in our days. How do we show the importance of the Torah? We stand up and kiss the Sefer Torah, the Torah scroll, when it is removed from the Ark. We stand up when a Torah scholar approaches us. He is a living Sefer Torah. Most importantly, we learn Torah with all our strength. We listen to Torah classes and lessons. We stretch our minds to understand Hashem's Word. And we review it many times until we remember it. It becomes a part of us. It sinks into our bones and our hearts. And it guides our lives. Kinderlach, may you all be adorned with the glorious crown of Torah.

A Personal Visit

"Moshe went and spoke these words to all of Israel" *(Devarim 31:1)*. Where did Moshe go? This well-known question is asked by many of the commentators. The K'li Yakar answers that Moshe Rabbeinu was going to encourage everyone to do *t'shuva* (correct their sins). Everyone has some character traits that need work. It is so difficult for a person to see his own faults. Most people will not go to a rabbi to ask him which sins they should correct. Even if a rabbi speaks to a group of people, they usually will not take it to heart. Therefore, Moshe went to each tent individually. He spoke heart-to-heart to each family about doing *t'shuva*.

> *Kinderlach . . .*
> *Moshe Rabbeinu visited people personally to encourage them to do t'shuva. Sometimes we must make a personal visit for a different reason. We are all involved in doing t'shuva before Yom Kippur. The last mishnah in Tractate Yoma states that Yom Kippur atones only for sins between man and Hashem (for instance, eating non-kosher food). As for sins between people (such as stealing or speaking lashon hara) we must first go to the person and ask him for forgiveness.*
> *On the other hand, we must forgive people even if they do not ask. Tefilla Zakka is the prayer that we say before Yom Kippur begins. This prayer includes a declaration of forgiveness to all those who have wronged us. Let us all forgive everyone, so they will not have to come and ask for forgiveness. That is a true act of kindness. May Hashem be kind to us and grant us all a* gemar chasima tovah, *that we should be sealed in the Book of Life.*

The Shadow

"Chaim, watch out. Something is following you."

"Uh oh! How big is it, Chaim?"

"It's about your size."

Avi's stomach begins to get queasy. Something that big is following him? What is it?

"What should I do, Chaim? Should I try to run away from it?"

"No, you'll never succeed."

"Should I hide?"

"You can. It will not follow you into your hiding place. But when you come out, it will be waiting for you."

"How can I escape from this thing, Chaim?"

"The truth is that you can't, Avi. You'll never shake it. However, it is very good for you to have it around. It helps you a lot. More than you'll ever know."

"Now you've really got my curiosity going. What is this thing?"

"It is . . . your shadow."

"My shadow. I see. It follows me everywhere. I can never escape from it. That makes sense. But please tell me, Chaim—how is my shadow good for me?"

"That is a deep subject, Avi. The HaEmek Davar speaks about it in this week's parasha."

"Now you've really got my curiosity going. How is my shadow related to Parashas Vayelech?"

"The verse states: '. . . because Hashem your God travels with you . . .' (*Devarim* 31:6). The HaEmek Davar explains that this verse is referring to Hashem's *hashgacha pratis*, His Personal Providence concerning the life of every Jew. He 'travels' with us, so to speak, guiding the events of our lives.

Just like a shadow always travels with a person, so too He always travels with us."

"That can be a frightening thought. If we do something wrong, Hashem is right there."

"Yes. However, this will ultimately bring a person to great success. When he knows that Hashem is watching his every deed and is ready to reward or punish him immediately, he will learn to be careful and not sin."

"I see. Hashem is always 'shadowing' me, so to speak."

"Exactly."

Kinderlach . . .

Now we have a new way to remember Hashem. Walk outside in the bright sun and look at your shadow. It is always with you, following you around wherever you go. So too, Hashem is always "shadowing" you with hashgacha pratis. He is taking care of you, rewarding you for every mitzvah that you do, and, Heaven forbid, the opposite. Don't forget your shadow, kinderlach. And don't forget Hashem. Who can even think of sinning, knowing that Hashem is always "shadowing" him?

Parashas Haazinu

Listen Carefully

"Why are you crying, Chaim?"

"My ear hurts, Mommy. Oww, oww."

"Oh, my dear Chaim. Let's put some drops in and give you some aspirin. Then let us say the special prayer to remind us that Hashem is sending the cure. That should make you feel better."

"Thank you, Mommy."

"While we are waiting for the medicines to work, let me tell you a word of Torah which will take your mind off the pain, Chaim. The parasha begins with the words 'Give ear, O heavens, and I will speak' (*Devarim* 32:1). The Midrash Rabba teaches us a few things about listening."

"I'm listening, Mommy."

"Good, Chaim. The Midrash says that if you want to avoid sickness in your ears or in any of the limbs of your body, turn your ears to listen to words of Torah."

"I'm listening, Mommy."

"In the days of the Midrash, people would give a nice scent to their clothes by burning some incense in a special container with many holes. The clothes were spread on top of the container and they absorbed the fragrance of the incense. This one container could hold many clothes. The ear is like this special container. When it listens to words of Torah, it gives life to all 248 limbs of the body, just as the container gives a beautiful aroma to all of the clothes."

"That is wonderful, Mommy. I want to hear more."

"Listen to words of Torah and learn them well. When you open your mouth to speak words of Torah, people will listen to you. Moshe Rabbeinu went up to Har Sinai to listen to Torah from Hashem's mouth. When Moshe began to speak, the heavens and earth quieted to listen to him. As the verse says, 'Give ear, O heavens, and I will speak; and may the earth hear the words of my mouth' (*Devarim* 32:1)."

Kinderlach . . .

Listening is a wonderful quality. When you listen to someone carefully without interrupting, you are paying him the greatest respect. Listening to words of Torah is even better. It gives life and health to your whole body, and makes you wise and respected. Begin by making an extra effort to listen to Daddy's and Mommy's words of Torah. Your teachers also deserve the utmost respect and attention. Your friends and study partners can teach you much Torah. As the Mishnah (Pirkei Avos 4:1) states, "Who is a wise person? One who learns from everyone." Listen to them.

Your Place in History

"Oh nations, sing the praises of His people . . ." *(Devarim 32:43)*. The verse states that the nations of the world will praise the Jewish people. Why will they praise us? Which deeds will they see as praiseworthy? Rashi explains that they will see how Hashem has tested His nation with many trials and tribulations. Through all of this, we have not abandoned Him. That is what the nations will realize, and they will pay tribute to the Jewish people.

Let us see how we react to tests. It is quite commendable when someone passes the entrance exam to be admitted to a school. Passing the final exams after the first year of study is more of an accomplishment. Getting passing grades in graduation exams, receiving advanced degrees, and *semicha* (Rabbinical ordination) are all accomplishments that reflect years and years of hard work and self-sacrifice.

Now take a look at Jewish history. Read and learn the *Tanach* (Bible). Then study the events of the Second Temple Period, Middle Ages, Crusades, Renaissance, leading up to the present day. You will see that the Jewish people have undergone many, many tests, much more difficult than school exams. Each new phase of our history has had its own unique challenges. Yet we have risen to them all. Throughout 3,500 years of nationhood, we have neither abandoned Hashem nor His Torah. Knowing this strengthens our faith in Hashem. Facing challenges is not new. We are not the first generation to face challenges. Just as our ancestors successfully met theirs, so will we meet ours.

> *Kinderlach . . .*
> *As you study history, you will see the glory of the Jewish people and our loyalty to Hashem. You are part of a people whose greatness has shone over 3,500 years. We have our own tests in our days. We know where we stand and we know what we have to do. We are part of the Jewish people. We have our place in history.*

Deep Meaning

"Okay, let's go over this again, Chaim. Who was the sister of Lotan?"

"Ummm . . .Addah?"

"No, she was the mother of Elifaz."

"Ummm . . . Bosmat?"

"No, she was the mother of Reuel. Do you want to try again, or do you want me to tell you the answer?"

"Please tell me, Daddy."

"Timna was the sister of Lotan."

"Now I remember. Daddy. May I ask you a question?"

"Of course, Chaim."

"I hope it is not out of line."

"Don't worry, Chaim."

"Why do I have to know who the sister of Lotan was? I know that it is written in the Torah, but do I need to know everything that is written in the Torah? Aren't some things more important than others?"

"Chaim, Rashi address that very question in this week's parasha."

"Really? Where?"

"The verse states: 'For it (the Torah) is not an empty thing for you. For it is your life' (Devarim 32:47). Empty? Who would ever think that the Torah is empty, Heaven forbid?"

"No one, Daddy."

"Exactly, Chaim. Therefore, this verse must be teaching us something a little deeper. Rashi explains this point by using the very same verse that we are learning. Timna was from a royal family. Her brother, Lotan, was one of the princes of Seir. She could have married one of the princes of her own nation. Yet, she chose instead to be a concubine to Esav, descendant of Avraham. This shows the greatness of Avraham Avinu. Timna would rather be a concubine in Avraham's house than a princess in her own nation."

"Wow, Daddy."

"Yes, Chaim. Rashi here in Parashas Haazinu explains that nothing in the Torah is empty of meaning. If you search, you will be rewarded. Our Sages found deep meaning to the words, 'And Timna was the sister of Lotan.'"

"Daddy, you have given me a whole new perspective on my studies. All the Torah that I learn is very meaningful. If I don't see the meaning right away, I just have to search a little harder."

"Chaim, with an attitude like that, you are on your way to becoming a Torah scholar."

> Kinderlach . . .
> What is the excitement of receiving a gift? Unwrapping it. Sometimes there are several layers of wrapping paper. As you remove each one, your excitement grows. Sometimes the deeper meaning of a verse or a mishnah or a gemara is "hidden." We have to get to work "unwrapping" it. Layer by layer. Until we get to the gift. A real treat. Enjoy those sweet words of Torah, kinderlach. They are the best.

Parashas Vezos Haberachah

Unconditional Love

"Yossie, I may never see you again."

The son tried to hold back his tears.
"I want to tell you one last thing."
"Yes, Daddy."
"I love you with all of my heart."

Yossie's heart was breaking.
"But Daddy, I caused you so much aggravation. I kept getting into trouble and you had to bail me out."
"It doesn't matter. I love you."
"But Daddy, how can you not have any resentment? The reason you are suffering is because of me."
"Yossie, I love you. Please come close to me, I want to bless you."

Yossie could contain himself no longer. He broke down and cried like a baby. His father's true love pierced his heart.

"And this is the blessing that Moshe, the man of God blessed the Children of Israel before he died" (Devarim 33:1). Why does the Torah begin the verse with the word, "and", which is a word that connects two ideas? This is the beginning of the blessing. How is it connected to the previous section, where Moshe Rabbeinu is informed that Hashem's decree has been finalized, and he will not enter the Land of Israel? The Ohr HaChaim HaKadosh answers this question by pointing out a very deep connection between these two events.

A person's nature is to resent those who cause him trouble. The Children of Israel committed many a sin during the forty years that Moshe led them. Yet he kept after them, and saved them every time. Until ultimately, they put him in a situation where he sinned, and lost the opportunity to enter the Land of Israel. His heart longed for the Holy Land more than we can ever imagine. Therefore, we can surely understand if he harbored resentment toward the Jewish People. Yet Moshe Rabbeinu had *savlanut*, patience. He harbored no resentment. The verse tells us an even more astounding aspect of Moshe Rabbeinu's character. Not only did he not resent the Children of Israel, he loved them and he blessed them. "And this is the blessing." The blessing comes along with the preceding decree. Moshe's love was not deterred one bit.

Kinderlach . . .
This is unconditional love. No matter what happens, I love you. This is the love of a parent for a child. This is the love of Hashem for the Jewish people. Quite a high spiritual level. We can appreciate it, and even try to reach for it ourselves. Love every Jew. Give to them and watch your love grow. Every good improvement in this area is a mighty accomplishment. Learn to give unconditional love.

Strong Glue

"Oh no."

"What happened?"

"I broke this plate."

"Maybe we can fix it. Let's have a look."

"Here are two big pieces, which fit together on most of the broken spot. There are just a few gaps where the pieces do not fit."

"I have some strong glue that can put this plate back together. Due to the gaps, weak glue cannot work. However, strong glue can overcome the gaps."

"[It is] the inheritance of the congregation of Yaakov" (*Devarim* 33:4). "When will the Torah be upheld?" asks the Baal HaTurim. "When the congregation of Yaakov is gathered together." The Ramban adds that the Torah describes the descendants of Yaakov as a congregation. We should congregate—gather together—to learn and teach Torah. Then it will be an eternal inheritance for us.

Sometimes it seems so difficult to gather together. Where is the "strong glue" that used to unite people through thick and thin? In truth, we have much more in common than we realize. We are like the plate that almost fits together perfectly. Strong glue—a desire to focus on the similarities—will overcome our differences and hold us together. If we focus on the minor differences between us, we will never achieve unity. Weak glue will not hold this plate together.

> *Kinderlach . . .*
> *Torah is our family inheritance. And it will continue to be so, as long as we gather together to learn and teach these holy words. Gathering together requires glue. Let's make some strong glue today. Take turns around the table listing the things that we have in common. Every one of them is a reason to stick together. Get stuck today, kinderlach, with glue so strong that you'll never come apart.*

United We Stand

"Kinderlach, today you are going to see something that you have never seen before. Something truly amazing."

"What is it, Daddy?"

"Wait a little longer, Chaim. We will be there soon, with Hashem's help."

"That is my bottle of drink!"

"No! It is mine! Give it back to me!"

"No! You took it from me!"

"Rivkie and Sari. Why are you fighting in the back seat of the car?"

"She took my drink bottle. Do you see? My name is on the bottle."

"Rivkie is right, Sari. Now please give the bottle back to her and apologize for taking it away."

"But I am so thirsty, Daddy."

"Why don't you ask Rivkie nicely for a drink from her bottle? I am sure that she will give it to you."

"Rivkie, I am sorry that I took your bottle. May I please have a drink?"

"Of course, Sari. My pleasure."

"Girls, making peace is so important. You will see that right now. We have arrived."

"Daddy, we are at the ocean. We have been here before."

"Yes but look over there where the boats are docked. Do you see anything unusual?"

"Yes, Daddy! A big house floating on the water."

"Not exactly, kinderlach. That house is built on boats. The builder tied two boats together, then began building the house on top of them. Isn't it magnificent?"

"Wow."

As the children are watching, the ropes holding the boats together become untied. The boats begin to drift apart. Suddenly the house has no support. In a few short moments, the whole beautiful structure goes tumbling into the water.

"Daddy, what a tragedy."

"Baruch Hashem no one was hurt. We can all learn something from this, kinderlach."

"We have to tie tight knots."

"True, but there is more to learn than that, Chaim. The Sifrei explains a verse in this week's parasha with a story very similar to what happened today. 'He became King in Yeshurun when the numbers of the nation gathered – the tribes of Israel in unity' (*Devarim* 33:5)."

"Let me guess. The King is Hashem."

"Right, Sari. When the Jewish people are united here in this world, then Hashem's Holy Name is praised in Heaven. The structure in Heaven has its foundations down here. Just like the house built on the boats. As long as the boats are connected, the house stands. The minute they come apart, it falls into the ocean. That is why it was so important that you made peace in the car. Peace among the Jews is the strong foundation upon which Hashem's kingship is built."

Kinderlach . . .
What a fitting way to end and begin the Torah. The Creation begins with peace. As we say in our morning prayers, "He makes peace and creates everything." And it ends with peace among the Jewish people. May we all merit to build that peace that will crown Hashem as King in Yeshurun and herald the coming of the Messiah speedily in our days.

Index

A

accounting, 122
aggravation, 177
Aharon, 80, 111, 121, 144, 148, 162, 269
ahavas chinam, 35 (see also love)
Ammon, 286
anger, 238
appreciation, 126
argument, 213
Aron HaKodesh, 189
assign responsibility, 277
Avinu Malkeinu, 276
Avraham, 19, 21, 26, 254, 264, 286, 288, 313

B

Baal HaTurim, 101, 133, 271, 317
Balak, 225
bar mitzvah, 194, 225
Bartenura, 237
Beis Din, 101
Beis HaMikdash, 133, 140, 277, 302
Beit Kinesset, 222
best friend, 197
Betzalel, 120
bikur cholim, 21
Bilaam, 227, 228, 231, 257, 286
Binding of Yitzchak, 19
Bircas HaMazone, 268
bitachon, 146 (see also Trust)
blessing, 33, 61, 62, 63, 65, 66, 136, 145, 258, 267, 280, 292, 315
boss, 202, 219, 220
bris 21, 300
burning bush, 72

C

carelessness, 97
cave, 108
cell phone, 259
census, 235
center of our lives, 191
chacham leiv, 124
Chafetz Chaim, 6, 7, 16, 17, 73, 114, 151, 153, 156, 158, 177, 190, 195, 197, 245, 294, 299
change yourself, 82
Chanukah, 255
charity, 73, 82, 105, 107, 123
Chasdei Hashem, 193
cheating, 33, 164
cheating, 33
chessed, 116
chutzpah, 135
close relationship, 132
clothing, 111, 112
compassion, 287
compliment, 63
compromise, 100
consideration, 98, 125, 194
constant mitzvos, 264
constructive criticism, 257
Cossacks, 285
covenant, 300
craftsman, 15, 155
creation of the world, 5
curiosity, 235
cursing, 164

D

Da'as Zekeinim MiBaalei
   HaTosfos, 257, 274
damage, 97
danger, 94, 98, 111, 288
deal falsely, 164
death of a tzaddik, 269
deep meaning, 312
desert, 92, 119
despair, 211
diamonds, 116
diet, 232
dignity, 111, 229, 231 (see also
   tznius, modesty, proper dress)
dispute, 213
Divine Presence, 22, 37
dream, 35, 47, 53

E

education, 61
Efraim, 61, 65
Egypt, 45, 52, 57, 62, 66, 78,
   80, 85, 87, 112
Eisav, 33, 43
elderly people, 131
Elul, 275
embarrass, 133, 194
emotions, 67
emunah, 241
encouragement, 80
eternity, 88, 107
exception, 159
exile, 36

F

fairness, 216
family, 285
feelings, 134, 167, 177
flattery, 245
following rules, 159

forgive, 60

G

Garden of Eden, 190
gematria, 237
generosity, 117
gift shop, 176
giving, 167
good habits, 281
good name, 120
gossip, 164
gradual change, 243
gratitude, 58, 123, 285
growth (spiritual), 28
grudge, 60, 164

H

HaEmek Davar, 307
hakhel, 303
halachah, 191
happiness, 82, 173, 282, 284,
   292, 293
Har Sinai, 201, 310 (see also Mt.
   Sinai)
Hashem is our Father, 273
Hashem loves us, 166, 182
Hashem's children, 273,
Hashem's protection, 86
hashgacha pratis, 53, 192, 307,
   308
hatred, 164, 178
heart, 83, 85, 88, 90, 93, 105,
   124
heaven, 140, 151
help other Jews, 272
hidden miracles, 90, 139
holiness, 71, 111
homework, 71, 76, 126
honesty, 125
honor, 21, 42, 65

honoring Hashem, 63
honoring our parents, 43, 94
humility, 134, 135

I

Ibn Ezra, 121
improving yourself, 16, 18
Imrei Emes, 149
influence, 50
ir miklat, 247

J

jealousy, 146, 148, 195
job, 198, 202, 212, 216, 227
joy, 174
judging carefully, 33, 50

K

Kiddush Hashem, 169
Kiddush, 235, 272
kindness, 59, 87, 90, 116, 269, 284, 287, 305
King David, 36
king, 46
K'li Yakar, 54, 88, 192, 301, 304
Koheles, 120
Korach, 213, 217
korbanot, 132, 137, 233
Kriyat Shema, 222

L

ladders, 211, 212
Land of Israel, 37, 58, 62, 73, 208, 211, 227, 244, 253, 316
lashon hara, 7, 151, 152, 153, 154, 156, 158, 208, 255, 262, 305 (see also proper speech, shmiras ha'lashon)
Leah, 42, 63

learning Torah, 6, 15, 62, 91, 261, 292, 298, 303
Lekach Tov, 204
life-and-death, 296
listening, 75, 78, 93, 104, 181, 271, 309
listening to your parents, 95
lost objects, 284
Lot, 286
love (unconditional), 315
love your fellow Jew, 164
love yourself, 165
love, 8, 36, 59, 63, 66, 167, 315
loving Hashem, 265
loving mitzvos, 8
loyalty to Hashem, 312
lulav, 235
lying, 164

M

machlokes, 213, 214
Maharal, 59
makkos, 85
Malbim, 16, 35, 37, 80, 88, 104, 144, 244, 254, 297
mashiach, 36
matza, 235
Mechilta, 86
Megillah, 235
memories, 84
Menashe, 61
menorah, 110
mensch, 229
meraglim, 211
mercy, 115
Meshech Chochma, 86
Mesillas Yesharim, 146
midbar, 244
middos, 134, 146, 149 (see also anger, appreciation, bitachon, carelessness, chessed,

chutzpah, compassion, consideration, giving, gratitude, happiness, hatred, humility, joy, love, loyalty, modesty, patience, plugger, politeness, pride, punctuality, respect, savlanut, shalom, tznius, well-mannered)
Midrash Rabba, 213, 258, 309
Midrash, 42, 43, 110, 120, 197, 258, 309
milk and honey, 115
miracles, 84, 89, 140, 142
Mishkan, 110, 119, 122, 125, 132, 135, 144, 163, 189, 190, 195, 255
missile, 150
mission, 123
Moav, 227, 228, 286
modesty, 39, 42, 112, 231, 241, 242 (see also tznius, dignity, proper dress)
mood, 174
Moshe Rabbeinu, 36, 72, 78, 121, 125, 134, 144, 163, 195, 213, 217, 239, 254, 257, 260, 304, 310, 316
Mt. Sinai, 92 (see also Har Sinai)
music, 104
mussar, 209

N

national mitzvah, 303
nedarim, 184
Nesivos Shalom, 28
next world, 88, 290
Noam Elimelech, 89

O

obsession, 225

Ohr HaChaim, 65, 66, 67, 163, 274, 294, 316
Olam Habba, 107, 151, 290
old-age home, 131
onaas devarim, 177
Orchos Tzaddikim, 292
overcoming difficulties, 71

P

panic, 296
patience, 244, 282, 316 (see also savlanut)
peace, 79, 137, 196, 217, 223, 262, 276, 318
Pele Yo'etz, 112, 174, 184
Pesach, 82, 85, 95
Pirkei Avos, 93, 263, 310
plagues, 78, 80
plugger, 51
polishing gems, 202
politeness, 282
positive thinking, 50
possessions, 98
pray for others, 294
prayer, 29, 32, 33, 55, 57, 59, 219, 259, 260, 276, 281, 294, 305, 309, 320
pride, 159
prison, 46, 47, 53, 54, 62, 285
privacy, 230
proper dress, 112 (see also tznius, modesty, dignity)
proper speech, 6, 155 (see lashon hara, shmiras ha'lashon)
property, 97, 100
punctuality, 282
punishment, 76, 216, 245,

Q

quickness, 117, 120

R

Rabbeinu Bechaye, 32, 54, 125, 267
raffle, 117
Ramban, 19, 192, 239, 240, 245, 286, 317
Rashi, 86, 120, 124, 201, 211, 231, 239, 261, 273, 311, 313
Rav Chaim Shmuelevitz, 204
Rav Eliyahu Dessler, 132, 167
Rav Leib Chasman, 116, 124, 258
Rav Moshe Aharon Stern, 13
Rav Moshe Feinstein, 9, 62, 123, 211
Rav Shimshon Refael Hirsch, 241, 257
Rav Yisrael Salanter, 209
redemption, 35
refuah shelayma, 20, 33
remembering Hashem, 278
remembering Torah, 261, 263
resentment, 316
respect, 282, 310
responsibility for other Jews, 301
responsible, 98
returning lost objects, 284
revenge, 60, 164, 216, 218, 241, 248
reward and punishment, 181, 216, 246
reward for learning Torah, 298
reward for mitzvos, 235, 270
reward greater when difficult, 71
reward, 11, 19, 21, 43, 57, 202, 217, 235
Rivkah, 32, 36
role model, 63
Rosh Hashanah, 115
Rosh Hashanah, 54, 184, 272, 276, 301

rules, 159

S

sacrifice, 131, 233
safety, 288
Sanhedrin, 15
savlanut, 316 (see also patience)
school bell, 200
school, 200, 201, 203, 209, 214, 230
Sea of Reeds, 86, 89
search team, 298
see the positive, 53
Sefer HaChinuch, 60, 82, 142, 164, 265, 277, 280, 287, 303
Sefer Torah, 189
self improvement, 81
Selichos, 294
sensitivity, 133
setbacks, 244
S'forno, 274
Shabbos, 9, 24, 39, 61, 85, 112, 120, 225, 278, 288, 290, 293
shadow, 305
shalom, 136, 223
Shechina, 144, 223
Shema, 59, 261, 265
Shir HaShirim, 275
Shlomo HaMelech, 135, 146
shmiras ha'lashon, 151 (see also lashon hara, proper speech)
shmitta, 179
shofar, 235
siddur, 57
Sifrei, 245, 261, 320
sign, 85, 114
silence, 156
Simchas Torah, 13
Sin of the Golden Calf, 254
sinas chinam, 35, 36, 37 (see also hate)

613 mitzvos, 43, 82, 142, 171, 179, 262, 292
slave, 87
smile, 75, 81, 105
soul, 144
speaking softly, 80, 240
speech, 3, 6 (see also lashon hara, proper speech, shmiras ha'lashon)
spies, 208, 211, 255
spiritual level, 11, 13
splitting the sea, 89
stealing, 164, 246
study partner, 94, 116
Succos, 13, 302
swearing falsely, 164

T

Tabernacle, 110, 119, 122, 125, 189, 195, 255
teaching Torah, 14
Tefilla Zakka, 305
tefillin, 235
Tehillim, 206, 260, 284, 293
tests, 19, 33, 53, 58, 63, 311
thanking Hashem, 63, 266, 278
the home, 42, 46, 47
Thirteen Attributes of Mercy, 116
Tisha B'Av, 256, 296
tochacha, 257
Torah and mitzvos, 197
Torah as our guide, 108
Torah Temima, 263
Toras Chaim, 190
train station, 204
Tree of Life, 190
trickery, 33, 157
trust in Hashem, 146 (see also bitachon)
trustworthy, 126
try your hardest, 209

tsedaka, 105, 117, 235, 237, 278, 280
t'shuva, 38, 86, 87, 116, 296, 297, 298, 304, 305
tzaddik, 225, 237, 244, 269, 288
tzitzis, 235
tznius, 111 231, 241, (see also modesty, dignity proper dress)

U

unity, 36, 276, 301, 317, 320

V

vandalism, 100
visiting the sick, 21
vows, 184

W

war, 293
wealth, 194, 195, 203, 266, 298, 299, 300
well-mannered, 169
wisdom, 124

Y

Yaakov, 33, 35, 38, 43, 57, 61, 65, 258, 317
Yalkut Shimoni, 116, 267
Yamim Noraim, 13
yeshiva, 24, 27
yetzer hara, 21, 38, 88, 149, 163, 165, 208, 215, 240, 293
yetzer hatov, 208
Yitzchak, 32, 36
Yom Kippur, 254, 305
Yosef, 52, 53, 54, 57, 58, 59, 60, 62, 65, 66, 87, 88, 121
your job, 248

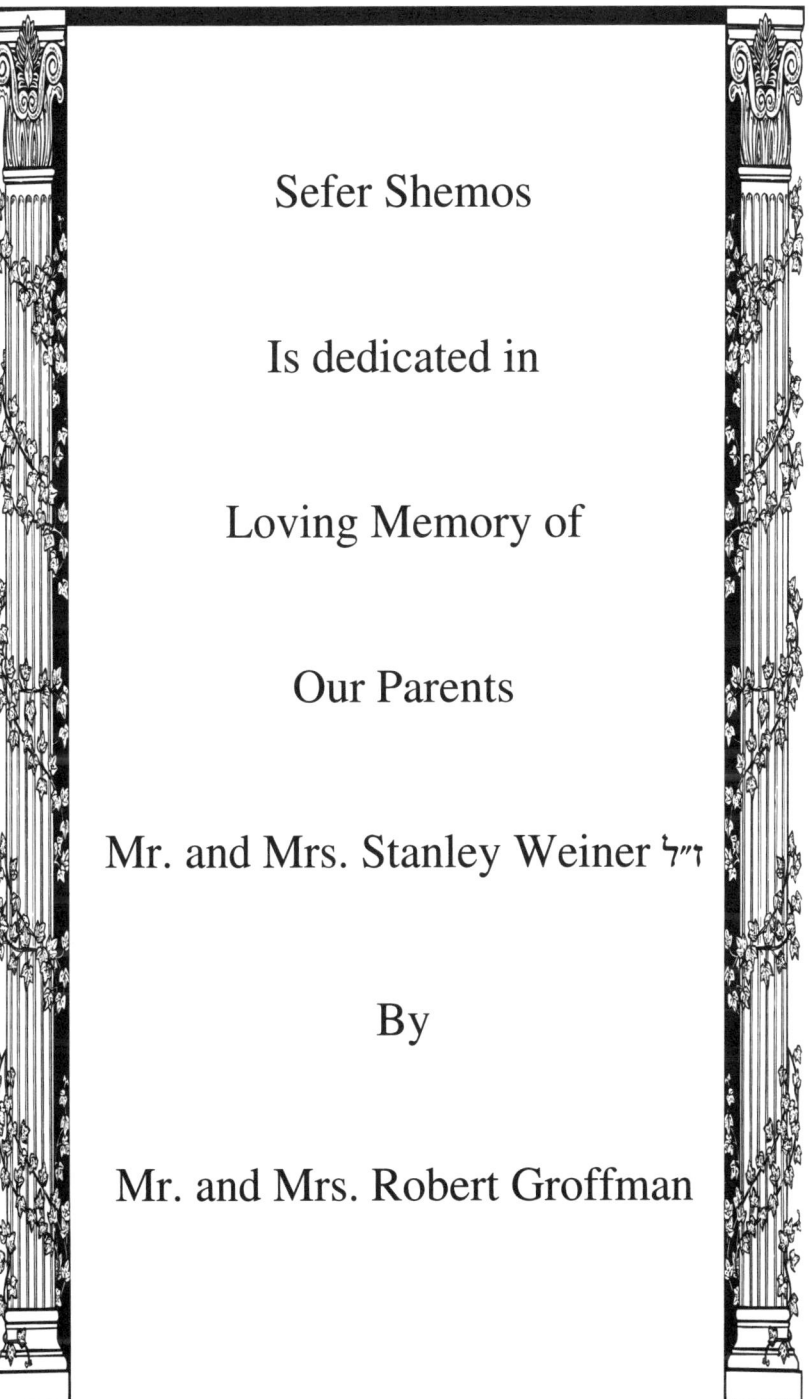

Sefer Shemos

Is dedicated in

Loving Memory of

Our Parents

Mr. and Mrs. Stanley Weiner ז״ל

By

Mr. and Mrs. Robert Groffman

Sefer Vayikra

Is dedicated in

Loving Memory of

Our Parents

Mr. and Mrs. Victor Groffman ז״ל

By

Mr. and Mrs. Robert Groffman

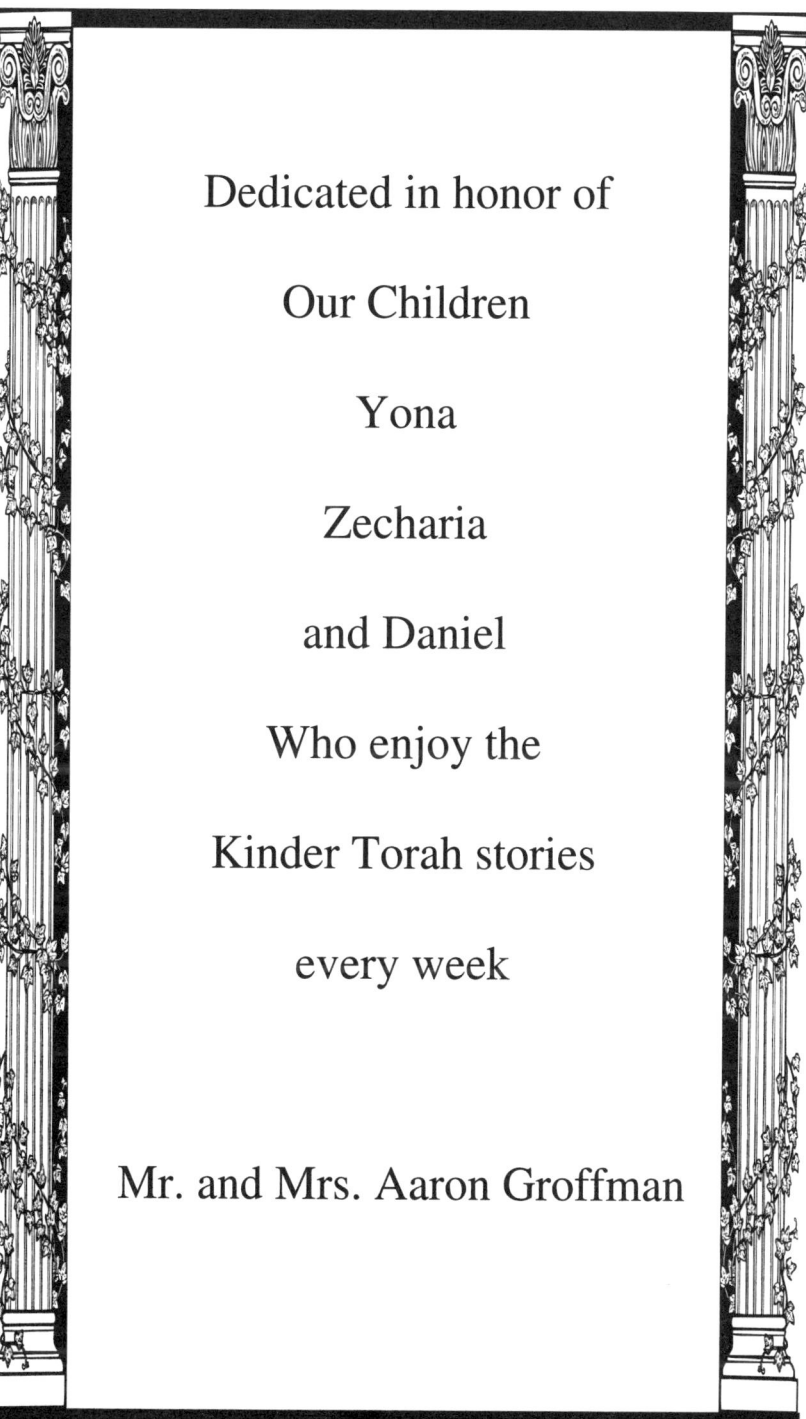

Dedicated in honor of

Our Children

Yona

Zecharia

and Daniel

Who enjoy the

Kinder Torah stories

every week

Mr. and Mrs. Aaron Groffman

Dedicated to our Parents and Grandparents
Calvin and Lila Glustoff עמו"ש
Max and Mollie Superstein ז"ל
From their children
Judi, David, Eli, and Meira
Superstein

In Loving Memory of
Shimi Schwartz ז"ל
Boris Glassman ז"ל
Zehava Lurie ע"ה
Hillel Libauer ז"ל
Dedicated by the Glassman and Schwartz
families of Israel, South Africa, Canada,
Australia, Zimbabwe.

לע"נ
מרת פריידא בת ר' מרדכי ע"ה
Mrs. Freda Aaronson
נלב"ע עש"ק כ"ה תמוז תשל"ה
Dedicated by her children
ת. נ. צ. ב. ה.

In Loving Memory of
Our Father
Louis J. Sinowitz ז"ל

Dedicated לע"נ
Sonny Goodman
שמעון בן אברהם צבי הלוי ז"ל
נפטר הושענא רבה תשכ"ח

פרשת חיי שרה
מוקדש לע"נ
שרגא פייבל בן יצחק ז"ל

Dedicated in Loving Memory of
My Uncle
Aaron Cohen ז"ל
From Daniel Cohen

From Mrs. Malka Shafer

From Mrs. Batia Nadel

Hatzlacha from Cousins Mirele and Melvin
Steinig, Rabbi Sholom and Judy Steinig,
Jay and Ann Greenberg.

Hatzlacha Rabba from Mr. And Mrs. Feder
Beit Shemesh

לע"נ ר' יעקב בן אליהו שרגא ז"ל
ת. נ. צ. ב. ה.

Hatzlacha Rabba
From Mr. Aaron Elbogen

Hatzlacha Rabba
From Mr. Yitzchok Friedland

Wishing Hatzlacha to our dear friend Simcha
and his family in all his Chizukei HaRabim
and this lovely Sefer. From Family Alexander.
לעילוי נשמת הלן בת רחל ע"ה